Research on Intelligent Manufacturing

Research on Intelligent Manufacturing (RIM) publishes the latest developments and applications of research in intelligent manufacturing—rapidly, informally and in high quality. It combines theory and practice to analyse related cases in fields including but not limited to:

Intelligent design theory and technologies
Intelligent manufacturing equipment and technologies
Intelligent sensing and control technologies
Intelligent manufacturing systems and services

This book series aims to address hot technological spots and solve challenging problems in the field of intelligent manufacturing. It brings together scientists and engineers working in all related branches from both East and West, under the support of national strategies like Industry 4.0 and Made in China 2025. With its wide coverage in all related branches, such as Industrial Internet of Things (IoT), Cloud Computing, 3D Printing and Virtual Reality Technology, we hope this book series can provide the researchers with a scientific platform to exchange and share the latest findings, ideas, and advances, and to chart the frontiers of intelligent manufacturing.

The series' scope includes monographs, professional books and graduate textbooks, edited volumes, and reference works intended to support education in related areas at the graduate and post-graduate levels.

More information about this series at http://www.springer.com/series/15516

Jiajie Guo · Kok-Meng Lee

Flexonics for Manufacturing and Robotics

Modeling, Design and Analysis Methods

Huazhong University of Science and Technology Press

 Springer

Jiajie Guo
School of Mechanical Science and
 Engineering
Huazhong University of Science and
 Technology
Wuhan, China

Kok-Meng Lee
The George W. Woodruff School of
 Mechanical Engineering
Georgia Institute of Technology
Atlanta, GA, USA

ISSN 2523-3386   ISSN 2523-3394 (electronic)
Research on Intelligent Manufacturing
ISBN 978-981-13-2666-0   ISBN 978-981-13-2667-7 (eBook)
https://doi.org/10.1007/978-981-13-2667-7

Jointly published with Huazhong University of Science and Technology Press, Wuhan, China
ISBN: 978-7-5680-4054-9

The print edition is not for sale in China Mainland. Customers from China Mainland please order the print book from: Huazhong University of Science and Technology Press.

Library of Congress Control Number: 2018956272

This Springer imprint is published by the registered company Springer Nature Singapore Pte Ltd.
The registered company address is: 152 Beach Road, #21-01/04 Gateway East, Singapore 189721, Singapore

Preface

With the increasing demands for smart machines and intelligent equipment adaptable to humans and environments, compliant structures and flexible electronics have been widely developed in robotics and thin-wall components with a large strength-to-weight ratio are common in manufacturing. Among different challenges in flexible mechatronics (flexonics), modelling, design and analysis are still critical issues to be dealt with because of the nonlinear complexity of continuum. This book formulates distributed models in both time and spatial domains using a geometric approach, along with practical field-based sensing methods for robotics and manufacturing. Applications are illustrated by examples of exoskeletons, mobile sensor network, intelligent sensing, and so on. This book is written for university researchers, R&D engineers and graduate students in engineering and science, who wish to learn the core principles, theories, technologies, and applications of flexonics. It can be served as a textbook or reference for a graduate level course on mechatronics, which may require prerequisites of linear algebra, mechanics of materials, ordinary and partial differential equations, numerical methods, and vibrations.

The text is organized into seven chapters. Chapter 1 is an introduction to flexonics with basic concepts, problems and reviews of related work. Chapter 2 presents fundamentals of mathematics for modelling, design and analysis of flexonics. Chapter 3 formulates the boundary value problems for basic flexible elements of beams and plates. Application examples are given in the last four chapters. Chapter 4 illustrates the design of a mobile node as an application of flexonics for structural health monitoring, where design concepts, functionalities, experimental validation and demonstrative examples are included. Chapter 5 presents a distributed-parameter method for intelligent sensing of displacement and strain distributions across a flexible thin-wall workpiece and their field reconstruction for real-time manufacturing applications. Chapter 6 provides a bio-joint model to capture the kinematic and dynamic features of a biological joint, based on which an adaptive exoskeleton is designed to eliminate negative effects associated with the closed leg-exoskeleton kinematic chain on a human knee. Chapter 7 presents a modelling method to capture musculoskeletal deformations and its immediate application is illustrated with poultry meat deboning in food processing. As a unified modelling and analysis approach is developed in Chaps. 2 and 3, readers can find commons among the various examples in subsequent chapters and may probably extend the presented method to applications that are not covered in this book. Chapters 4–7 are somewhat independent from each other, so some of them can be skipped or chosen based on readers' application needs and interests.

Many findings in this book are based on the last decade of research conducted at Georgia Institute of Technology and Huazhong University of Science and Technology, and they were obtained under research grants supported by the Georgia Agricultural Technology Research Program, National Science Foundation (Grant CMMI-0928095) and more recently, the National Basic Research Program of China (973 Program, Grant 2013CB035803) and the National Natural Science Foundation of China (Grants 51505164, 51875221). The authors wish to acknowledge with great appreciation the colleagues and graduate students for their collaboration or suggestions in the presented research, like Prof. Yang Wang, Dr. Dapeng Zhu, Dr. Xiaohua Yi and Yang Xie for Chap. 4, Prof. Kun Bai, Prof. Jingjing Ji, Man Yu, Wuguang Liu, Ruochu Liuand Bo Wang for Chap. 5, Dr. Donghai Wang for Chap. 6, and Dr. Jungyoul Lim and Mark Claffee for Chap. 7. The writing of this book is funded by Hubei Academic Works Publishing Special Fund and National Science and Technology Academic Works Publishing Fund. The authors would also like to thank Daokai Yu from HUST Press and all the committee members for their efforts to organize this book series which makes publication of this book possible.

Wuhan, China   Jiajie Guo
Atlanta, USA   Kok-Meng Lee

Contents

About the Authors

Jiajie Guo received the B.S. degree from the Department of Engineering Mechanics and Science at Peking University, Beijing, China, in 2006, and M.S. and Ph.D. degrees from Mechanical Engineering, Georgia Institute of Technology, Atlanta, GA, USA, in 2009 and 2011, respectively. He is currently an Associate Professor in the State Key Lab of Digital Manufacturing Equipment and Technology and the School of Mechanical Science and Engineering at Huazhong University of Science and Technology, Wuhan, Hubei, China. He is IEEE and ASME member and a program committee member of IEEE/ASME International Conference on Advanced Intelligent Mechatronics. His current research interests include human-centered robotics, flexible mechatronics, manufacturing, and system dynamics/control. He has published more than thirty peer-reviewed technical papers in journals and conferences and has been awarded the best paper award from IEEE/ASME Transaction on Mechatronics in 2015 and the "Most Practical SHM Solution for Civil Infrastructures" Video Award in Action session of the 8th International Workshop for Structural Health Monitoring in 2011.

Kok-Meng Lee received the B.S. degree from the State University of New York, Buffalo, NY, USA, in 1980, and the S.M. and Ph.D. degrees from the Massachusetts Institute of Technology, Cambridge, MA, USA, in 1982 and 1985, respectively. Currently, he is a Professor in the George W. Woodruff School of Mechanical Engineering at the Georgia Institute of Technology, Atlanta, a member of the Thousand Talents Plan in the Organization Department of the Central Committee, and a Distinguished Professor in the School of Mechanical Science and Engineering at Huazhong University of Science and Technology, Wuhan, China. His research interests include system dynamics/control, robotics, automation, and mechatronics. He is a world renowned researcher with more than 30 years of research experience in magnetic field modeling and design, optimization and implementation of electromagnetic actuators. He has published over 150 peer-reviewed papers and he holds eight patents in machine vision, three degrees of freedom (DOF) spherical motor/encoder, and live-bird handling system. He is IEEE/ASME Fellow and was the Editor-in-Chief for the IEEE/ASME Transactions on Mechatronics from 2008 to 2013. Recognitions of his research contributions include the National Science Foundation (NSF) Presidential Young Investigator, Sigma Xi Junior Faculty Research, International Hall of Fame New Technology, and Kayamori Best Paper awards.

Abbreviations

2D   Two dimensional
3D   Three dimensional
AWM   Automated wing manipulation
BJC   Bio-joint constraint
BVP   Boundary value problem
CBM   Curvature-based beam model
DOF   Degrees of freedom
FEA   Finite element analysis
IVP   Initial value problem
MSM   Multiple shooting method
ODE   Ordinary differential equation
PDE   Partial differential equation
SHM   Structure health monitoring

Symbols

Capitalized Symbols

A	Cross-sectional area
C	An instantaneous contact point
E	Young's modulus
G	Shear modulus
I_1, I_2, I_3	Moment of inertia
J	Moment of inertia
L	Beam length
N_r	Number of rigid bodies in a multi-body system
N_c	Number of compliant beam in a multi-body system
P_s	Material point on the initial beam axis
Q_s	Material point on the deformed beam axis
XYZ	Global reference coordinate frame
$\mathbf{E}_1, \mathbf{E}_2,$ and $\mathbf{E}_3$	Unit vectors along global reference frame X, Y, and Z axes, respectively
$\mathbf{F} = [F_1 \ F_2 \ F_3]^T$	External force acting on a compliant beam
$\mathbf{K}^{(0)}$	Curvature of the initial beam
$\mathbf{K}^{(e)}$	Curvature change due to elastic deformation
$\mathbf{K}$	Curvature of the deformed beam
$Skew(\mathbf{K})$	$\begin{bmatrix} 0 & k_3 & -k_2 \\ -k_3 & 0 & k_1 \\ k_2 & -k_1 & 0 \end{bmatrix}$
$\mathbf{M} = [M_1 \ M_2 \ M_3]^T$	External moment acting on a compliant beam
$\mathbf{R}, \mathbf{R}^{(0)}$	Rotational matrix
$\mathbf{X}$	State variables

Lower Case Symbols

a, b, c	Length of principal axis of an ellipsoid
b	Beam width
h	Beam thickness
k	Curvature
m	Mass
p	Pitch
r	Radius of an osculating circle at contact point
r_w	Wheel radius
s	Undeformed path length from the beam root to the reference point
t	Time
$x_s, y_s,$ and z_s	x_s is the longitudinal axis; y_s and z_s are the principal axes of the cross-sectional area in the initial beam
$\mathbf{e}_1^{(0)}, \mathbf{e}_2^{(0)}$ and $\mathbf{e}_3^{(0)}$	Unit vectors along principal axes of $x_s, y_s,$ and z_s, respectively
$\mathbf{e}_1, \mathbf{e}_2$ and $\mathbf{e}_3$	Unit vectors along principal axes of $\xi_s, \eta_s,$ and ζ_s, respectively
$[\mathbf{e}_T, \mathbf{e}_N, \mathbf{e}_B]$	Frenet–Serret frame where $\mathbf{e}_T$ is the tangent unit vector, $\mathbf{e}_N$ is the normal unit vector, and $\mathbf{e}_B$ is the binormal unit vector
$\mathbf{f}$	External force acting on a rigid body
$\mathbf{q}_F$	Distributed force
$\mathbf{q}_M$	Distributed moment
$\mathbf{x}^{(0)} = \left[x_1^{(0)} \; x_2^{(0)} \; x_3^{(0)}\right]^T$	Global nodal coordinates of initial beam shape
$\mathbf{x} = [x_1 \; x_2 \; x_3]^T$	Global nodal coordinates of deformed beam shape

Greek Symbols

Γ	Boundary of a rigid body
α, β	Angles
κ	Curvature
τ	Torsion, external moment acting on a rigid body
ψ, θ and φ	Euler angles
$\xi_s, \eta_s,$ and ζ_s	ξ_s is the longitudinal axis; η_s and ζ_s are the principal axes of the cross-sectional area in the deformed beam
ρ	Density
υ	Poisson ratio
ω	Angular velocity
ε	Longitudinal strain on the beam axis
μ	Friction coefficient

Subscripts and Superscripts

(e)   Elastic deformation
(0)   Initial state

List of Figures

List of Tables

Chapter 1
Introduction

1.1 Background and Motivation

Flexible mechatronics is an electro-mechanical system composed of flexible elements which are subjected to large deformations and capable of transferring forces, torques and energies. They have been widely used in many engineering applications in terms of compliant mechanisms such as snap-fits [1], micro grippers [2] and flexure hinges [3]. In recent years, flexible or compliant devices have attracted more and more attention to biology related applications, such as flexible electronics, bio inspired robotics and food processing industry, because compliant components exhibit many advantages in dealing with highly deformable biological materials over rigid engineering tools in terms of simple structures and light weights. While multi-body flexible structures can achieve a large range of motions and are energy efficient because of being free from contact frictions, their designs are difficult to analyze and often based on assumptions (such as small deformation and fixed rotation center) in order to reduce nonlinear problems to more tractable forms to be solved in a lumped-parameter approach. Such simplified analyses generally yield only first-order approximation, and are unable to capture complicated behaviors such as the coupled effects among bending, twisting, and contact with joint clearances.

1.2 Problem Description and Objectives

With the emerging applications in mind, there is a need to develop a modeling method for designing and analyzing flexible mechatronics systems. Although many methods are available in modeling flexible structures, challenges still exist in the following aspects:

© Huazhong University of Science and Technology Press, Wuhan and Springer
Nature Singapore Pte Ltd. 2019
J. Guo and K.-M Lee, *Flexonics for Manufacturing and Robotics*, Research on
Intelligent Manufacturing, https://doi.org/10.1007/978-981-13-2667-7_1

(1) The distributed models for flexible elements are too complicated for design analysis and automatic control in practice.
(2) Typical numerical methods for analyzing flexible deformations, such as finite element (FE) methods, are usually time-consuming with non-optimal performance.
(3) Nonlinear material and geometrical properties give rise to challenges in modeling and analysis of biology-related systems in engineering applications.

By understanding the current limitations and challenges, the objectives of this book seek to resolve these issues in the following ways:

(1) Distributed models are formulated for flexible components, specifically beam and plate elements, where continuous physical fields on flexonics can be captured with the theoretical models featuring infinite degrees-of-freedom.
(2) A common approach to study the behaviors of flexible structures is to solve the formulated boundary value problems for various applications with the multiple shooting method (MSM). It is also desired to highlight the technique to simplify a distributed model with finite degrees-of-freedom in frequency analysis.
(3) Results and recent developments in flexonics research are presented to illustrate the applications of the formulated models and theoretical methods.

1.3 Review of Related Work

Compliant mechanisms have a long history and can be found in our daily life in numerous applications (such as catapults, bows, binder clips, diving boards and clocks). A comprehensive review of compliant mechanisms is beyond the scope for this book. The reviews conducted for this research focus on practical issues related to engineering applications in manufacturing and robotics. In relation to these applications, several problems arise for designing compliant mechanisms. For example, two dimensional (2D) models of engineering mechanisms are not suitable for characterizing complex three dimensional (3D) biological apparatuses. Assumptions such as small deformation are no longer adequate for design analysis of compliant structures involving large deformations and nonlinear dynamic behaviors. Moreover, typical engineering designs based on fixed rotation centers or standard cylindrical/sphere geometries cannot fully capture the natural properties of bio-joint constraint. Typical biological joints can attain limited translational motions in addition to the three rotational freedoms due to the deformability of connective tissues. Given the complex assembly with clearances, a biological joint is often compliant and has more degrees of freedom (DOF) than an engineering joint [4, 5]. Existing ball-socket approximations are often inadequate to characterize biological joints and their associated bio-skeleton kinematics. Thus, the contact point between these extraordinary shapes, in general, is difficult to locate.

Given the dimension of the above difficulties, the remaining review is organized with topics on compliant mechanisms, joint constraint, numerical methods for boundary value problems, flexible robotics for structural health monitoring, human-centered equipment, process state monitoring for manufacturing and poultry-meat processing.

1.3.1 Modeling of Compliant Mechanisms

Flexible beams are used as a fundamental component in many compliant mechanisms and have been modeled using different formulations. The pseudo-rigid-body approach [6] is among the most commonly used approximation, which extends the rigid body analysis by modeling the beam as a torsional spring connecting two rigid links. One of the difficulties in the pseudo-rigid-body approach is to find the beam equivalent stiffness and its location for modeling it as a torsional spring. Although errors of the tip deflection are within the 0.5% tolerance, it is not accurate about the displacement along the path length.

Distributed beam models for small deformations fall into two main categories: Euler–Bernoulli beam theory [7] and Timoshenko beam theory [8]. Euler–Bernoulli beam theory, as known as the classical beam theory, has been widely used to solve engineering problemswith conditions of material linear elasticity, small deformations, zero shear distortions. The theory also assumes that a cross section remains planar and normal to the reference beam-axis in both the undeformed and deformed configurations. Timoshenko beam theory takes shear deformations and rotational inertia effects into account, which is suitable for studying short beams or beams subject to high frequency excitation.

For formulating the large deflection of a 2D beam under various load conditions, Frisch-Fay [9] presented closed form solutions; as the solutions incorporate elliptic integrals, the calculation procedure is cumbersome. Although Frisch-Fay also presented some results for analyzing 3D beams, closed form solutions are still not available. Numerical methods are generally required to solve for 3D beam deformations. This research formulates the equations of motion for a 3D beam based on the model by Pai and Nayfeh [10] for solving using a MSM [11].

In analyzing flexible body dynamics, four groups of formulations have been developed to capture the large displacements and rotations of structural components:

(1) The floating frame of reference method [12] defines each body deformation with respect to their local body-fixed coordinate systems using modal representation or finite element (FE) methods.
(2) The incremental FE method uses infinitesimal rotations as nodal coordinates, which may not be correct to solve large rotation problems [13].

(3) The large rotation vector method employs large rotation coordinates in the inertial frame, which leads to a simple expression for the kinetic energy but results in redundant representation of derivatives of displacement coordinates besides the rotation coordinates [14, 15].

(4) More recently, the absolute nodal coordinate formulation which does not require interpolation of finite rotations has been widely used for FE analysis [16].

1.3.2   Joint Constraint

For compliant mechanisms involving contact, several questions must be answered: (1) Whether there is a contact? (2) Where is the contact? (3) What is happening during the contact? Numerical methods for determining contacts between rigid bodies fall into two formulations. The first is the penalty formulation utilizing the no-interpenetration condition, which avoids the solution existence questions and avoids impulses. The second is the time-stepping formulation that employs complementarity (or optimization) conditions to determine contact or not. Some reviews and recent developments on both formulations can be found from the works of Stewart [17, 18], Song [19], and Adly and Goeleven [20].

For contact problems involving flexible bodies, the two main formulations are the methods of variational inequality (VI) [21] and the variational equality (VE) [22], which have been investigated for frictionless and frictional contact problems respectively. When considering biological joints, contact kinematic problems arise because of the non-uniform shapes of joints. Kelkar et al. [23] quantitatively studied the translational motion of humeral head during the rotation of shoulder joints. Similar results of tibia translational motion in human knee joints are observed in experiments by Iwaki et al. [24]. Yang and Meng [25] employed a 3D friction contact model for planar contact and developed analytical criteria to determine the transitions among stick, slip and separation of contact. Montana [26] studied the velocity of a rolling sphere between two grasping fingers of arbitrary shapes.

Unlike an engineering joint where assembled parts are usually concentric cylinders or spheres, biological joints are often a complex assembly of two or more different shaped components as shown in Table 1.1 [27]. Bio-joint geometries have also been mathematically described for bio-medical and surgery; see for examples, [24, 28, 29]. With the development of non-contact scanning technologies (such as MRI and laser beams), relatively accurate 2D and 3D bone geometries can be obtained. However, most real biological joints are approximated by simple geometries (circles and spheres) [24, 29] in order to reduce their highly nonlinear kinematics to a more tractable form. The oversimplified ball-socket approximation generally neglects the joint clearance, and cannot account for deformable effects needed for applications such as breast-meat deboning where percent yields (hence highly precise cutting) are of particular concern.

Table 1.1 Joints and corresponding models

Hip joint	Elbow joint	Metacarpopha-langeal joint
Ball-socket	Hinge	Condyloid
Atlantoaxial joint	Carpometa-carpal joint	Acromio-clavicular joint
Pivot	Saddle	Plane

With rapid advances in robotics and mechatronics, exoskeletons have been widely developed to assist in or rehabilitate human body motions; for examples, the commercialized Lokomat [30] for treadmill training, assistant exoskeleton [31] for elderly persons, hybrid assistive limb [32] to assist in walking and climbing, the ankle-foot orthosis powered by artificial pneumatic muscles [33], and the Berkeley lower extremity exoskeleton [34] to assist in carrying heavy loads over rough terrain. Experiments [35] on a robotic exoskeleton controlled by muscle activity could be useful tools for testing neural mechanism of human locomotor adaptation. While mechanical exoskeletons have the advantages of adding energy to human motions and adjusting motion patterns, it could perturb normal motions and potentially cause pain or even damage to human joints. To minimize negative effects of an artificial exoskeleton on human joints, the design and control of rehabilitation exoskeletons require a good understanding of the natural bio-joint kinematics and kinetics.

Natural bio-joints (that exoskeletons are designed to rehabilitate or assist) are commonly modeled in kinematics as non-slip revolute joints (such as a pin or ball joint). Unlike an engineering joint which typically has a fixed rotational center, bio-joints often consist of non-uniform shaped contact parts that roll and slide. Human bodies also vary widely in shapes and sizes and change over years; engineering joints are usually not compliant to accommodate these variations. Although exoskeletons help users adapt their motion after repetitive training, there are potentials for damages to bio-joints in long term usage if natural joint variations are not accounted for.

Compliant mechanisms that reduce assembled joints (and thus friction) can be employed in exoskeletons to accommodate shape, size and motion variations in human joints. "Soft" pneumatic muscle actuators are used as power sources [36], and flexible cables are used for transmission in a lower-extremity powered exoskeleton [37]. However, most of the works on compliance have been motivated by power efficiency rather than the interaction between a human body and an exoskeleton. As a result, recent works, for example flexible geared joints and rubber footpads [38], incorporate elements for shock absorption. Besides providing assistive power, an exoskeleton should not interfere negatively with normal human-joint motions; otherwise, it could result in discomfort and potential damages. For these reasons, problems on interaction between bio-joints and compliant mechanism are worthy of exploration.

Among challenges in the modeling of human-body motions are the characterization of the joint mechanics and musculoskeletal geometries [39]. Different experimental methods have been developed to detect joint structures, and measure the knee joint motions [40]. These include the most commonly used skin-marker systems [41, 42] where soft tissues often make them difficult to apply, and the radiation radiographic/fluoroscopic techniques [43, 44]. More recently, the electromagnetic techniques (MRI) [24] provide a way to shed light on the internal geometries of joints. With geometrical details of a joint available from experiments, kinematic models can be built for analyses. A computer model with surface friction [45] was suggested showing that the condylar geometries could have important differences in kinematics, function and wear. Accurate solutions of tibiofemoral contact behaviors were obtained from a 3D finite-element model [46]. Recently, a computational model allowing for anatomical details was built using CAD/CAE methods to predict the lower leg kinematics [47].

Motivated by the need to provide a good understanding on the interaction between natural joints and artificial mechanisms for design and control of exoskeletons, this book presents a mathematical bio-joint model originally proposed [4] for mechanical deboning of chicken breast meat [5].

1.3.3 Numerical Methods for Boundary Value Problems

The shooting method (SM) was first proposed by Keller [48] to solve the boundary value problem (BVP) of ordinary differential equations (ODEs). It transforms the BVP into an initial value problem (IVP) by guessing the unknown initial values first, and then utilizes Newton's methods to iteratively re-evaluate the initial guesses to "shoot" at the terminal values. Like most iterative methods for nonlinear problems, the convergence of SM is also sensitive to the initial guesses. To reduce the solution sensitivity to the initial guesses and thus improve the convergence property, Keller [48], Stoer and Bulirsch [49] developed the multiple SM by dividing the integration region into smaller sections and performing SM within each section. The continuity of the pieced solutions is guaranteed by adding new constraints on the boundaries of each section, so it greatly increases the scale of the problem size.

Some improved SMs have been proposed in recent years. Holsapple et al. [50] used modified SM to "shoot" at intermediate values until the solution matched its terminal value. A generalized SM (GSM) developed by Lan and Lee [51] included unknown parameters into the formulation in order to solve compliant mechanisms of flexible links in series. Liu [52] used Lie-Group SM to solve BVP with multiple solutions. Most of the SM applications have been devoted to the design analysis of flexible beams and frames [11, 53–56], in which SM is used to study the deflection of the compliant beam rather than the dynamics in the time domain. Although Lan et al. [56] formulated the partial differential equation (PDE) for dynamic analysis, GSM is still limited to solve deformed shape along the path length. SM has been designed to solve ODEs, and little efforts have been made to extend it to solving PDEs until recent years. Chang [57] solved a heat conduction problem with SM; and Liu [58] identified the damping and stiffness by transforming an ODE to PDE.

1.3.4 Flexible Robotics for Structural Health Monitoring

In recent years, wireless sensor networks have attracted growing interest for the structural health monitoring (SHM) of civil structures [59]. The leap from traditional cable-based sensing systems to wireless sensor networks can significantly reduce installation time/cost, and potentially enable dense instrumentation and bring unprecedented improvements to structural monitoring. As another transformative change to sensor networks, the next revolution is predicted to be networks of mobile sensor nodes (MSNs) [60]. In a mobile sensor network, each MSN can be a sensor-carrying robot capable of autonomously exploring surroundings and exchange information with peers through wireless communication. Motivated by these emerging needs, this book presents a design method for developing flexure-based MSNs [61, 62] for negotiating obstacles (such as corners, reinforced ridges) while moving on ferromagnetic surfaces for SHM applications [63].

As field robots have been attracting increasing interests in replacing human labor in a hazardous or high-risk working environment, three issues are of the most concern in the design; adherence, mobility and flexibility. Using magnetic devices and vacuum suction cups are two major methods to attach a robot on a working surface. Backes et al. [64] designed a robot for visually inspecting aircraft exterior using suction cups for adherence and ultrasonic motors for mobility to crawl on a 2D surface. In Shang et al. [65] the prototype robot was designed with suction cups for adherence to crawl on non-ferrous surfaces to inspect aircraft wings and fuselages. Other attaching methods include aerodynamic attraction [66] and biomimetic approach [67]. Based upon magnetic on-off robotic attachment devices, a magnetic walker has been developed for maneuvering on a 2D surface [68]. In order to inspect carbon steel pipe, a magnetic wheeled robot has been developed to move automatically along the outside [69] and inside [70] of piping. Using an induction pin, a magnetic wheeled robot can be easily detached by manipulating the magnetic flux direction [71]. For steel pipe inspection, a magnetic actuator incorporating with shape-memory-alloy coils has been developed to move in the complicated environment of pipes [72]. Most existing wheeled robots for similar applications are often designed and analyzed under small deformations to avoid nonlinearity of lateral bending and buckling. However, robots designed based on rigid components often have limited range of motions thus are not adaptable to complicated working environments. While designs based on rigid links/joints simplify analyses, they potentially limit the versatile functionality of a robot. To overcome this difficulty, the multi-agent network of self-assembly modular robots [73] provide a flexible architecture and relevant control methods for coordinated motions [74, 75]. This book offers an alternative solution to design compliant structures allowing large deformations to provide flexible manipulation of a wall-climbing robot and improve mobility and flexibility of an MSN for SHM. While illustrated in the context of a mobile sensor node, this design concept can potentially enhance the flexibility of existing modular robots.

Compliant structures can also be found in flexible robots; see for examples [76–79] where focuses have been on modeling and control. Various compliant mechanisms have been studied for robot development, owing to the advantage of having no relative moving parts and thus no contact frictional dissipation [79, 81–84]. For commanding robot movements through real-time feedback, control strategies have been developed based on various modeling methods [85], including rigid body motions [77, 86, 87], vibration modes [88], and finite element methods [89, 90]. In many compliant mechanisms, flexible beams are used as a fundamental component. For a 2D beam capable of large deflections under various load conditions, closed form solutions can be found in [9]; however, expressed in terms of elliptic integrals, these solutions are computationally cumbersome for use in design and real-time control. More recently, a 3D beam model was developed in [91] and solved through the multiple shooting method (MSM) [11, 49]. Early work concerning the stability and buckling was motivated by structure design and analysis [7, 92]. Given the instability nature of buckling, its occurrence is usually not desirable; as a result, most studies have been concentrated on the critical forces and load-displacement relation of buckling mechanisms [93]. With few exceptions (such as Batoz and Dhatt [94] where the post-buckling equilibrium was analyzed), very little work has been conducted on displacement relations in large deflections and buckling analysis of flexible beams.

At Georgia Tech, the design of a flexure-based mechatronic (flexonic) robot for SHM has led to the development of an flexonic mobile node (FMN) [61, 62]. As analyzed in [80], the FMN utilizes large deflections and buckling of a compliant beam enabling it to flexibly negotiate different kinds of obstacles (such as abrupt angle changes) commonly encountered in complex civil structures. These attractive features found in the FMN provide the motivation for further studies in this book, which will be illustrated as an example of a multi-body compliant mechanism.

1.3.5 Human-Centered Equipment (Exoskeleton)

Exoskeletons have been widely studied in mechatronics and robotics for rehabilitating and assisting human body motions. Applications include an adaptive wearable ankle robot for the treatments of ankle sprain through physical rehabilitation [95], a wearable multiphalanges device for post-stroke rehabilitation [96], cable-driven arm exoskeleton [97], and active leg exoskeleton [98] facilitating stroke patients neuromotor training gait to improve their functional walking abilities. Although an exoskeleton or orthosis can assist or adjust a human musculoskeletal system, there are potentials for discomfort and injuries if it is not adaptive to the wearer. To reduce any negative effect from a rigid exoskeleton on a human biological joint (bio-joint), physical forces/torque acting on the human bio-joints must be well understood.

Exoskeleton designs are often based on assumptions that simplify bio-joints to engineering joints to reduce kinematic complexity to a tractable form. For example, knee-joints are commonly modeled as a pin-joint which has only one DOF [99] with a fixed rotation axis. However, knee-joints have a non-uniform geometry with varying articulating surfaces and non-constant rotation axes. In the crossed four-bar linkage model [100], the knee geometry is defined to consist of anterior cruciate ligament (ACL), posterior cruciate ligament (PCL), femur and tibia. A three-dimensional analytical model taking into account the knee-joint surface geometry can be found in Wismans et al. [101]. For standardization in a clinical joint coordination system, the knee joint is described with six-DOFs [102]. When designing a lower-extremity exoskeleton joint, the natural knee kinematics must be considered.

The human knee instrumented with a two-link mechanism forms a closed kinematic loop. Unlike the case of an open kinematic chain (such as human walking with no exoskeleton) experiencing no impulse within the joint, a combined knee-exoskeleton tends to create a residual force if the DOFs of the exoskeleton are insufficient to compromise with that of a human joint to align the motion axis or any human-machine kinematic differences [103–107]. Although some ergonomic (passive or self-adjusting) joints [108, 109] are designed, an analytical model considering a bio-joint and the effect of exoskeleton on a human joint have not been well understood. Considering the knee joint with two-DOFs (rotation and translation), the closed kinematic chain experiences a singularity when the knee is fully extended introducing an impulsive knee force internally [110]. Design of a lower-extremity exoskeleton with insufficient knee-motion knowledge can disturb and even damage a human knee; thus, the bio-joint kinematics should be fully accounted for in exoskeleton designs.

Human knee kinematics has been widely analyzed by researchers with an interest to understand abrasion (or the effect of femur rolling or sliding on tibia). Due to human knee closure and complicity, traditional off-the-shelf sensors cannot be implanted directly in the joint capsule, which have led to the development of non-invasive, high-resolution MRI-assisted technology [24, 111] that facilitates interpreting the behavior of a knee joint [110]. This book presents the kinematic and dynamic models formulated in [112, 113] for analyzing misalignments of the rotational axes in a knee-exoskeleton structure so that negative effects of the exoskeleton on the knee joint can be effectively eliminated.

1.3.6 Process State Monitoring for Manufacturing

With increasing demands for products with high strength to weight ratio, thin-wall component machining has become common in aviation industries. A good understanding of the stress and deformation caused by the vibration and the cutting force between a machine tool and workpiece is an essential prerequisite for the machining of thin shell parts. Deformations are spatially distributed across the thin-wall workpiece during machining; the main causes of distortions are vibrations under cutting forces and machining-induced surface residual stresses that are among the critical problems [114]. Displacement and strain distributions in a thin-wall component due to external loads (such as cutting and clamping) play an important role in assessing residual stresses and surface integrity of a machined product. As a main feature in intelligent manufacturing equipment [115], field sensing is essential to online compensation with autonomous process parameter updating. Motivated by the interests to improve "first time yield" and manufacture components at a faster rate while minimizing scraps, this book presents a new non-contact approach to characterize the dynamic displacement and strain fields in real time for continuously monitoring their distributions across a disk workpiece during machining.

Machine vision with various advanced sensing principles has been used to capture field-based information. The shape and deformation of a vibrating structure can be captured with 3D digital image correlation methods [116]. With the known force-deflection characteristics, a force sensor has been developed by observing displacements of the selected points in the compliant mechanism with a CCD camera [117]. Out-of-plane deformations of a specimen were captured in real time via full-field shadow moiré images to study how residual strains were built up in an epoxy molding compound during manufacturing [118]. Employing piezospectro-scopic effects, where spectral emissions of photo-luminescent materials are sensitive to the strains or stresses, a portable system has been developed for non-contact in situ stress sensing [119]. An alternative to optic-based imaging methods (where the performance effectiveness depends on environmental conditions during machining) is to reconstruct physical fields numerically with discrete measurements. Intelligent robotics has been employed to collect field data for health monitoring of civil infrastructures [120]; such as a wall-climbing robot capable of impact-echo acoustic inspection for plate-like structures [121]. Typical field reconstruction methods numerically solve a boundary value problem (BVP) formulated with appropriate governing equations and boundary conditions interpolated from measured nodal information in the region of interests. The curvature-based beam model was employed to predict and control a soft robot which continuous deformations are numerically obtained by the shooting method [80]. The confluence algorithm was applied for constructing dynamic displacements of a rectangular plate using experimental measurements and a numerical model [122]. Finite element analysis (FEA) is one of the most common approaches to solve BVPs for predicting distributed dynamic responses with prescribed accuracy. However, most numerical methods for solving BVPs usually involve iterations at the expense of relatively long computational time thus not practical for real time applications. Combining FEA with statistical analysis, the time for simulating workpiece deflections under machining has been reduced from weeks to hours [123], but still it is too time costly for online computations.

The modal expansion technique that assumes displacements of a deformation or vibration as a linear combination of shape functions has been developed to improve computational efficiency. The displacement field of a wing-like plate was obtained with mode shapes and strain measurements for control applications and health monitoring [124]. Since mode shapes can be obtained in advance, a displacement field is reconstructed by evaluating each modal coefficient with an approximation of locally measured strains through a linear regression. Formulated using the variation principle to derive a displacement-strain relation, the three-dimensional (3D) deformed shape of a composite stiffened panel under a mechanical/thermal load was reconstructed in real time using an inverse-FEA with in situ surface strain measurements [125], where the least-square regression was used to fit the calculated strains in FEA with measurements [126]. Given the differential relations between displacements and strains/curvatures, the bending of a beam was estimated by strain measurements [127], and the large deformations of a beam were calculated with the curvatures [80, 128]. The 3D deflected shape of a needle was predicted with local axial-strains measured by an array of Fiber Bragg Grating sensors [129]. Strain sensing was employed as a cost-effective method to reconstruct deformations in structural health monitoring [130, 131]. With the displacement field obtained from strain data using the above shape sensing methods, the process can be reversed through a spatial differentiation of the displacements to reconstruct the strain fields. The global dynamic strains in a wind turbine was extracted in a photogrammetric approach where motions of optical targets along the vibrating blades were tracked by high speed cameras, while the reconstruction accuracy depended on numerous tracking points covering the whole structures [132]. Besides, other physical quantities can also be obtained from displacement or strain data, such as stresses [133] and forces [117, 134], as long as their constitutive relations are known for a given mechanism. Though efficient for real-time reconstruction, the above shape sensing methods generally rely on strain sensors attached on the measured surfaces of the targeted structures. For material removal applications particularly rotating disks in aircraft engines and structural components in airframes, where workpiece parameters (inertia, damping and stiffness) are time varying, it is desired to develop a non-contact method for robust field sensing during machining.

To avoid difficulties encountered in direct strain sensing, this book tales advantages of the non-contact eddy-current displacement sensing to reconstruct both the displacement and strain fields of a thin-wall compressor disk under lathe turning. Eddy-current displacement sensing has been found to be robust under machining conditions [135] and implemented for monitoring the spindle status of a computer numerically controlled (CNC) end milling machine [136]. Moreover, eddy-current dampers (ECD) have been developed to suppress beam-like structure vibrations [137, 138] providing a relatively large stability margin for tuning process parameters involved in machining thin-wall components. As compared to shape sensing with strain measurements, the method introduced here captures strain field dynamics with displacement data using a similar approach for displacement field reconstruction in [139]. To account for the geometrical changes due to material removal during machining, the mode shapes were numerically calculated and normalized by the plate thickness [135] for multiple cuts, and the mode-shapes of a stepped plate during one cut were investigated in [140]. In this book, the calculated mode-shapes are stored in an offline database for real-time reconstruction during machining.

1.3.7 Poultry-Meat Processing

Processing of natural products (such as poultry and meat) requires presentation of the target area for subsequent handling (such as cutting). Bone structures deform as a result of manipulation through bio-joints. A good application example is the deboning of chicken breast meat [141], where the shoulder joint must be accurately located to sever the ligaments and tendons. Although marketed deboning machines are available, these "hard automation" systems, in general, are not as dexterous as human labors in handling with highly deformable natural objects. Given the large size/shape variations in natural products, Sandlin [142] explored a method to correlate the bone locations relative to the external surface features using a combination of X-ray and machine vision images. He [143] investigated the feasibility to emulate human deboning chicken breast meat using a spherical wrist motor [144] by experimentally measuring their arm motion and wrist torque profiles. More recently, Claffee [145] experimentally studied the effect of pulling the wing of a chicken carcass (on a commercial fixture) on the shoulder height suggesting that musculoskeletal deformations cannot be neglected for precision deboning of chicken breast meat.

At Georgia Tech, Lee [146] introduced an analytical model of a compliant grasping mechanism for automated transferring of live objects [147], where multiple rubber fingers are employed to emulate a pair of human hands. For such a grasping problem, the contact location (between the flexible finger and object) and its corresponding force are not known a priori. To accommodate size and shape variations encountered in grasping live objects, several methods [51, 55] have been proposed to improve the prediction of the contact location and force due to a 2D flexible beam. More recently, Li and Lee [148] developed an adaptive meshless method (MLM) for analyzing stresses due to large deformable contacts on the products being handled. The adaptive MLM, which is similar to FE methods but requires no meshes, increases the nodal density in regions of high mechanical stresses. This research extends the studies to analyze contacts within a bio-joint, where both rolling and sliding occurs during contact between two non-engineering geometries.

Precision deboning requires a good understanding of compliant joints and their effects on fixture designs and biological product manipulations. To provide an essential basis for optimizing the design of a manipulating trajectory for effective cutting, a more realistic and yet general model is needed to characterize the bio-joint kinematics. The analysis method is presented in the context of poultry processing but also helps analyze the motion of cam mechanisms or engineering joints where wears and tears could result in clearances in the joint and/or non-circular elements.

1.4 Book Outline

The remainder of this book is organized as follows: Chap. 2 presents the mathematical fundamentals for the theoretical modeling and simulated analysis in subsequent chapters. Chapter 3 derives the governing equations for two typical flexible elements, namely the beam and plate elements, based on which the boundary value problems are formulated as well as the generalized constraint. Then, applications of the mechanics models are illustrated in each chapter, specifically flexible robotics for structural health monitoring in Chap. 4, intelligent sensing for manufacturing process state monitoring in Chap. 5, bio-inspired exoskeleton designed with a bio-joint model in Chap. 6, and musculoskeletal modeling for poultry-meat processing in Chap. 7.

References

1. S. Genc, R.W. Messler, G.A. Gabriele, A systematic approach to integral snap-fit attachment design. Concurrent Eng.-Res. Appl. **10**(2), 84–93 (1998)
2. V. Seidemann, S. Butefisch, S. Buttgenbach, Fabrication and investigation of in-plane compliant su8 structures for mems and their application to micro valves and micro grippers. Sens. Actuat. A-Phys. **97-8**, 457–461 (2002)
3. B.-J. Yi, G.B. Chung, H.Y. Na, W.K. Kim, I.H. Suh, Design and experiment of a 3-DOF parallel micromechanism utilizing flexure hinges. IEEE Trans. Robot. Autom. **19**(4), 604–612 (2003)
4. K.-M. Lee, J. Guo, Biological joint kinematic model for flexible deboning automation, *presented at the International Symposium on Flexible Automation (ISFA)* (Atlanta, GA, USA, 2008)
5. J. Guo, K.-M. Lee, Effects of musculoskeleton model on flexible deboning automation, *presented at the International Symposium on Flexible Automation (ISFA)* (Atlanta, GA, USA, 2008)
6. L.L. Howell, *Compliant Mechanisms*, 1st edn. (Wiley, New York, 2001)
7. J.M. Gere, S.P. Timoshenko, *Mechanics of Materials*, 4th edn. (PWS, Boston, 1997)
8. S.P. Timoshenko, On the transverse vibrations of bars of uniform cross-section. Philos. Mag. **43**(253), 125–131 (1922)
9. R. Frisch-Fay, *Flexible Bars* (Butterworths, Washington, D.C., 1962)
10. P.F. Pai, A.H. Nayfeh, A fully nonlinear theory of curved and twisted composite rotor blades accounting for warpings and three-dimensional stress effects. Int. J. Solids Struct. **31**(9), 1309–1340 (1994)
11. P.F. Pai, A.N. Palazotto, Large-deformation analysis of flexible beams. Int. J. Solids Struct. **33**(9), 1335–1353 (1996)
12. R.A. Laskin, P.W. Likins, R.W. Longman, Dynamical equations of a free-free beam subject to large overall motions. J. Astronaut. Sci. **31**(4), 507–527 (1983)
13. T.R. Kane, R.R. Ryan, A.K. Banerjee, Dynamics of a cantilever beam attached to a moving base. J. Guid. Control Dynam. **10**(2), 139–151 (1987)

14. J.C. Simo, L. Vuquoc, On the dynamics of flexible beams under large overall motions—the plane case.1. J. Appl. Mech. Trans. ASME. **53**(4), 849–854 (1986)
15. J.C. Simo, L. Vuquoc, On the dynamics of flexible beams under large overall motions—the plane case.2. J. Appl. Mech. Trans. ASME, **53**(4), 855–863 (1986)
16. A.A. Shabana, R.Y. Yakoub, Three dimensional absolute nodal coordinate formulation for beam elements: theory. J. Mech. Des. **123**(4), 606–613 (2001)
17. D.E. Stewart, Rigid-body dynamics with friction and impact, Siam Rev. **42**(1), 3–39 (2000)
18. D.E. Stewart, Convolution complementarity problems with application to impact problems. IMA J. Appl. Math. **71**(1), 92–119 (2006)
19. P. Song, P. Kraus, V. Kumar, P. Dupont, Analysis of rigid-body dynamic models for simulation of systems with frictional contacts. J. Appl. Mech.-Trans. ASME **68**(1), 118–128 (2001)
20. S. Adly, D. Goeleven, A stability theory for second-order nonsmooth dynamical systems with application to friction problems. J. Math. Pure. Appl. **83**(1), 17–51 (2004)
21. N. Kikuchi, J.T. Oden, *Contact Problems in Elasticity: A Study of Variational Inequalities and Finite Element Methods* (SIAM, Philadelphia, 1988)
22. T. A. Laursen, J.C. Simo, A continuum-based finite-element formulation for the implicit solution of multibody, large-deformation frictional contact problems. Int. J. Numer. Methods Eng. **36**(20), 3451–3485 (1993)
23. R. Kelkar, V.M. Wang, E.L. Flatow, P.M. Newton, G.A. Ateshian, L.U. Bigliani, R. J. Pawluk, C.C. Mow, Glenohumeral mechanics: a study of articular geometry, contact, and kinematics. J. Shoulder Elbow Surg. **10**(1), 73–84 (2001)
24. H. Iwaki, V. Pinskerova, M.A.R. Freeman, Tibiofemoral movement 1: the shapes and relative movements of the femur and tibia in the unloaded cadaver knee. J. Bone Joint Surg. **82B**(8), 1189–1195 (2000)
25. B.D. Yang, C.H. Menq, Characterization of 3d contact kinematics and prediction of resonant response of structures having 3d frictional constraint. J. Sound Vib **217**(5), 909–925 (1998)
26. D.J. Montana, The kinematics of contact and grasp. **7**(3), 17–32 (1988)
27. Joints and corresponding models. Available: http://ovrt.nist.gov/projects/vrml/h-anim/jointInfo.html
28. R. Huiskes, J. Kremers, A. Delange, H.J. Woltring, G. Selvik, T.J.G. Vanrens, Analytical stereophotogrammetric determination of 3-dimensional knee-joint geometry. **18**(8), 559–570 (1985)
29. N. Nuno, A.M. Ahmed, Three-dimensional morphometry of the femoral condyles. **18**(10), 924–932 (2003)
30. G. Colombo, M. Joerg, R. Schreier, V. Dietz, Treadmill training of paraplegic patients using a robotic orthosis. **37**(6), 693–700 (2000)
31. K. Kiguchi, K. Iwami, M. Yasuda, K. Watanabe, T. Fukuda, An exoskeletal robot for human shoulder joint motion assist. IEEE/ASME Trans. Mechatron. **8**(1), 125–135 (2003)
32. H. Kawamoto, Y. Sankai, Power assist method based on phase sequence and muscle force condition for hal. Adv. Rob. **19**(7), 717–734 (2005)
33. D.P. Ferris, J.M. Czerniecki, B. Hannaford, An ankle-foot orthosis powered by artificial pneumatic muscles. J. Appl. Biomech. **21**(2), 189–197 (2005)
34. A.B. Zoss, H. Kazerooni, A. Chu, Biomechanical design of the berkeley lower extremity exoskeleton (bleex). IEEE-ASME Trans. Mechatron. **11**(2), 128–138 (2006)
35. K.E. Gordon, D.P. Ferris, Learning to walk with a robotic ankle exoskeleton. J. Biomech. **40**(12), 2636–2644 (2007)
36. N.G. Tsagarakis, D.G. Caldwell, Development and control of a 'soft-actuated' exoskeleton for use in physiotherapy and training. Autom. Rob. **15**(1), 21–33 (2003)
37. J.F. Veneman, R. Ekkelenkamp, R. Kruidhof, F.C.T. van der Helm, H. van der Kooij, A series elastic- and bowden-cable-based actuation system for use as torque actuator in exoskeleton-type robots. Int. J. Rob. Res. **25**(3), 261–281 (2006)
38. K. Low, Initial experiments on a leg mechanism with a flexible geared joint and footpad. Adv. Rob. **19**(4), 373–399 (2005)

39. M.G. Pandy, Computer modeling and simulation of human movement. Annu. Rev. Biomed. Eng. **3**(1), 245–273 (2001)
40. A. Bull, A. Amis, Knee joint motion: description and measurement. Proc. Inst. Mech. Eng., Part H: J. Eng. Med. **212**(5), 357-372 (1998)
41. M. Lafortune, C. Lambert, M. Lake, Skin marker displacement at the knee joint. J. Biomech. **26**(3), 299 (1993)
42. T.-W. Lu, J. O'connor, Bone position estimation from skin marker co-ordinates using global optimisation with joint constraints. J. Biomech. **32**(2), 129–134 (1999)
43. C. Peterfy, J. Li, S. Zaim, J. Duryea, J. Lynch, Y. Miaux, W. Yu, H. Genant, Comparison of fixed-flexion positioning with fluoroscopic semi-flexed positioning for quantifying radiographic joint-space width in the knee: test-retest reproducibility. Skeletal Radiol. **32**(3), 128–132 (2003)
44. G. Li, S.K. Van de Velde, J.T. Bingham, Validation of a non-invasive fluoroscopic imaging technique for the measurement of dynamic knee joint motion. J. Biomech. **41**(7), 1616–1622 (2008)
45. S. Sathasivam, P.S. Walker, A computer model with surface friction for the prediction of total knee kinematics. J. Biomech. **30**(2), 177–184 (1997)
46. T.L.H. Donahue, M. Hull, M.M. Rashid, C.R. Jacobs, A finite element model of the human knee joint for the study of tibio-femoral contact. J. Biomech. Eng. **124**(3), 273–280 (2002)
47. P.C. Liacouras, J.S. Wayne, Computational modeling to predict mechanical function of joints: application to the lower leg with simulation of two cadaver studies. J. Biomech. Eng. **129**(6), 811–817 (2007)
48. H.B. Keller, *Numerical Methods for Two-Point Boundary-Value Problems*. (Waltham, Massachusetts, Blaisdell, 1968)
49. J. Stoer, R. Bulirsch, *Introduction to Numerical Analysis* (Springer-Verlag, New York, 1993)
50. R. Holsapple, R. Venkataraman, D. Doman, A modified simple shooting method for solving two-point boundary-value problems. in *IEEE Proceedings of Aerospace Conference,* vol. 6 (2003), pp. 2783-2790
51. C.-C. Lan, K.-M. Lee, Generalized shooting method for analyzing compliant mechanisms with curved members. J. Mech. Des. **128**(4), 765–775 (2006)
52. C.S. Liu, The lie-group shooting method for nonlinear two-point boundary value problems exhibiting multiple solutions. CMES-Comp. Model. Eng. Sci. **13**(2), 149–163 (2006)
53. C.M. Wang, S. Kitipornchai, Shooting optimization technique for large deflection analysis of structural members. Eng. Struct. **14**(4), 231–240 (1992)
54. S.R. Li, Y.H. Zhou, Shooting method for non-linear vibration and thermal buckling of heated orthotropic circular plates. J. Sound Vib. **248**(2), 379–386 (2001)
55. X. Yin, K.-M. Lee, C.-C. Lan, Computational models for predicting the deflected shape of a non-uniform, flexible finger. in *Proceedings of IEEE International Conference on Robotics and Automation (ICRA),* vol. 3 (2004), pp. 2963–2968
56. C.-C. Lan, K.-M. Lee, J.-H. Liou, Dynamics of highly elastic mechanisms using the generalized multiple shooting method: simulations and experiments. Mech. Mach. Theory, **44**(12), 2164–2178 (2009)
57. J. R. Chang, C.S. Liu,C.W. Chang, A new shooting method for quasi-boundary regularization of backward heat conduction problems. Int. J. Heat Mass Transf. **50**(11–12), 2325–2332 (2007)
58. C.S. Liu, Identifying time-dependent damping and stiffness functions by a simple and yet accurate method. J. Sound Vib. **318**(1–2), 148–165 (2008)
59. J.P. Lynch, K.J. Loh, A summary review of wireless sensors and sensor networks for structural health monitoring. Shock Vib. Dig. **38**, 91–128 (2006)
60. I.F. Akyildiz, W. Su, Y. Sankarasubramaniam, E. Cayirci, A survey on sensor networks. IEEE Commun. Mag. **40**(8), 102–114 (2002)

61. K.-M. Lee, Y. Wang, D. Zhu, J. Guo, X. Yi, Flexure-based mechatronic mobile sensors for structure damage detection, *presented at the 7th International Workshop on Structural Health Monitoring* (Stanford CA, USA, 2009)

62. J. Guo, K.-M. Lee, D. Zhu, Y. Wang, A flexonic magnetic car for ferro-structural health monitoring, in *the Proceedings of the ASME Dynamics Systems and Control Conference (DSCC)* (Hollywood, CA, 2009), pp. 481–487

63. D. Zhu, X. Yi, Y. Wang, K.-M. Lee, J. Guo, A mobile sensing system for structural health monitoring: design and validation. Smart Mater. Struct. **19**(5), 055011 (2010)

64. P.G. Backes, Y. Bar-Cohen, B. Joffe, The multifunction automated crawling system (MACS), in *Proceedings of IEEE International Conference on Robotics and Automation*, vol. 1 (1997), pp. 335–340

65. J.Z. Shang, T. Sattar, S. Chen, B. Bridge, Design of a climbing robot for inspecting aircraft wings and fuselage. Int. J. Ind. Rob. **34**(6), 495–502 (2007)

66. J.Z. Xiao, W. Morris, N. Chakravarthy, A. Calle, City-climber: a new generation of mobile robot with wall-climbing capability, in *Proceedings of SPIE Unmanned systems technology VIII, PTS 1 and 2*. vol. 6230, ed. (SPIE-Int Soc Optical Engineering, Bellingham, 2006)

67. Y. Ota, K. Yoneda, T. Tamaki, S. Hirose, A walking and wheeled hybrid locomotion with twin-frame structure robot, *presented at IEEE/RSJ International Conference on Intelligent Robots and Systems* (2002)

68. B. Esser, J. Miller, D. Huston, P. Bourn, Robotic systems for homeland security, in *Proceedings of SPIE Nondestructive Detection and Measurement for Homeland Security II*, vol. 5395 (San Diego, CA, 2004), pp. 134–142

69. T. Yukawa, M. Suzuki, Y. Satoh, H. Okano, Design of magnetic wheels in pipe inspection robot, *presented at IEEE International Conference on Systems, Man and Cybernetics (SMC)* (2006)

70. F. Tache, W. Fischer, G. Caprari, R. Siegwart, R. Moser, F. Mondada, Magnebike: a magnetic wheeled robot with high mobility for inspecting complex-shaped structures. J. Field Rob. **26**(5), 453–476 (2009)

71. S.C. Han, J. Kim, H.C. Yi, A novel design of permanent magnet wheel with induction pin for mobile robot. Int. J. Precision Eng. Manuf. **10**(4), 143–146 (2009)

72. H. Yaguchi, N. Sato, Globular magnetic actuator capable of free movement in a complex pipe. IEEE Trans. Magn. **46**(6), 1350–1355 (2010)

73. H. Wei, Y. Chen, J. Tan, T. Wang, Sambot: a self-assembly modular robot system. IEEE/ASME Trans. Mechatron. **16**(4), 745–757 (2011)

74. S. Liu, D. Sun, C. Zhu, Coordinated motion planning for multiple mobile robots along designed paths with formation requirement. IEEE/ASME Trans. Mechatron. **16**(6), 1021–1031 (2011)

75. H. Mehrjerdi, M. Saad, J. Ghommam, Hierarchical fuzzy cooperative control and path following for a team of mobile robots. IEEE/ASME Trans. Mechatron. **16**(5), 907–917 (2011)

76. S. Ahmad, Control of cooperative multiple flexible joint robots. IEEE Trans. Syst., Man, Cybern. **23**(3), 833–839 (1993)

77. M.A. Arteaga, B. Siciliano, On tracking control of flexible robot arms. IEEE Trans. Autom. Control **45**(3), 520–527 (2000)

78. M. Filipovic, M. Vukobratovic, Modeling of flexible robotic systems, *presented at International Conference on Computer as a Tool (EUROCON)*, vol. 2 (2005), pp. 1196–1199

79. J.G. Garcia, A. Robertsson, J.G. Ortega, R. Johansson, Sensor fusion for compliant robot motion control. IEEE Trans. Rob. **24**(2), 430–441 (2008)

80. J. Guo, K.-M. Lee, D. Zhu, X. Yi, Y. Wang, Large-deformation analysis and experimental validation of a flexure-based mobile sensor node. IEEE-ASME Trans. Mechatron. **17**(4), 606–616 (2012)

81. C.-C. Lan, C.-M. Lin, C.-H. Fan, A self-sensing microgripper module with wide handling ranges. IEEE/ASME Trans. Mechatron. **16**(1), 141–150 (2011)

82. M. Filipovic, M. Vukobratovic, Expansion of source equation of elastic line. Robotica **26**(6), 739–751 (2008)
83. U.-X. Tan, W.T. Latt, C.Y. Shee, W.T. Ang, A low-cost flexure-based handheld mechanism for micromanipulation. IEEE/ASME Trans. Mechatron. **16**(4), 773–778 (2011)
84. H. Xie, S. Régnier, Development of a flexible robotic system for multiscale applications of micro/nanoscale manipulation and assembly. IEEE/ASME Trans. Mechatron. **16**(2), 266 (2011)
85. S.K. Dwivedy, P. Eberhard, Dynamic analysis of flexible manipulators, a literature review. Mech. Mach. Theory **41**(7), 749–777 (2006)
86. G.J. Tuijthof, J.L. Herder, Design, actuation and control of an anthropomorphic robot arm. Mech. Mach. Theory **35**(7), 945–962 (2000)
87. L. Gaudiller, F. Matichard, A nonlinear method for improving the active control efficiency of smart structures subjected to rigid body motions. IEEE/ASME Trans. Mechatron. **12**(5), 542–548 (2007)
88. C. La-orpacharapan, L.Y. Pao, Fast and robust control of systems with multiple flexible modes. IEEE/ASME Trans. Mechatron. **10**(5), 521–534 (2005)
89. R. Caracciolo, A. Trevisani, Simultaneous rigid-body motion and vibration control of a flexible four-bar linkage. Mech. Mach. Theory **36**(2), 221–243 (2001)
90. A. Trevisani, M.E. Valcher, An energy-based adaptive control design technique for multibody-mechanisms with flexible links. IEEE/ASME Trans. Mechatron. **10**(5), 571–580 (2005)
91. P.F. Pai, A.H. Nayfeh, A fully nonlinear-theory of curved and twisted composite rotor blades accounting for warpings and 3-dimensional stress effects. Int. J. Solids Struct. **31**(9), 1309–1340 (1994)
92. J. Goodier, Torsional and flexural buckling of bars of thin-walled open section under compressive and bending loads. J. Appl. Mech. ASME. **9**(3), 103–107 (1942)
93. F. Jarrar, M. Hamdan, Nonlinear vibrations and buckling of a flexible rotating beam: A prescribed torque approach. Mech. Mach. Theory **42**(8), 919–939 (2007)
94. J.L. Batoz, G. Dhatt, Incremental displacement algorithms for nonlinear problems. Int. J. Numer. Methods Eng. **14**(8), 1262–1267 (1979)
95. P.K. Jamwal, S.Q. Xie, S. Hussain, J.G. Parsons, An adaptive wearable parallel robot for the treatment of ankle injuries. IEEE/ASME Trans. Mechatron. **19**(1), 64–75 (2014)
96. A. Chiri, N. Vitiello, F. Giovacchini, S. Roccella, F. Vecchi, M.C. Carrozza, Mechatronic design and characterization of the index finger module of a hand exoskeleton for post-stroke rehabilitation. IEEE/ASME Trans. Mechatron. **17**(5), 884–894 (2012)
97. Y. Mao, S.K. Agrawal, Design of a cable-driven arm exoskeleton (CAREX) for neural rehabilitation. IEEE Trans. Rob. **28**(4), 922–931 (2012)
98. S.K. Banala, S.K. Agrawal, S.H. Kim, J.P. Scholz, Novel gait adaptation and neuromotor training results using an active leg exoskeleton. IEEE/ASME Trans. Mechatron. **15**(2), 216–225 (2010)
99. A.M. Dollar, H. Herr, Lower extremity exoskeletons and active orthoses: Challenges and state-of-the-art. IEEE Trans. Rob. **24**(1), 144–158 (2008)
100. J. O'connor, T. Shercliff, E. Biden, J. Goodfellow, The geometry of the knee in the sagittal plane. Proc. Inst. Mech. Eng. H, **203**(4), 223–233 (1989)
101. J. Wismans, F. Veldpaus, J. Janssen, A. Huson, P. Struben, A three-dimensional mathematical model of the knee-joint. J. Biomech. **13**(8), 681–685 (1980)
102. G. Wu, P.R. Cavanagh, Isb recommendations for standardization in the reporting of kinematic data. J. Biomech. **28**(10), 1257–1261 (1995)
103. A.H. Stienen, E.E. Hekman, F.C. Van Der Helm, H. Van Der Kooij, Self-aligning exoskeleton axes through decoupling of joint rotations and translations. IEEE Trans. Rob. **25**(3), 628–633 (2009)
104. A. Schiele, F.C. Van Der Helm, Kinematic design to improve ergonomics in human machine interaction. IEEE Trans. Neural Syst. Rehabil. Eng. **14**(4), 456–469 (2006)

105. A. Schiele, An explicit model to predict and interpret constraint force creation in phri with exoskeletons, in *Proceedings of IEEE International Conference Robotics Automation (ICRA)* (Pasadena, CA, USA, 2008), pp. 1324–1330

106. A. Schiele, Ergonomics of exoskeletons: Objective performance metrics, in *Proceedings of 3rd Joint European Conference Symposium on Haptic Interface for Virtual Environment Teleoperator and System* (Salt Lake City, USA, 2009), pp. 103–108

107. N. Jarrasse, G. Morel, Connecting a human limb to an exoskeleton. IEEE Trans. Rob. **28**(3), 697–709 (2012)

108. L.E. Amigo, A. Casals, J. Amat, Design of a 3-dof joint system with dynamic servo-adaptation in orthotic applications, in *Proceedings of IEEE International Conference on Robotics Automation (ICRA)* (Shanghai, China, 2011), pp. 3700–3705

109. D. Cai, P. Bidaud, V. Hayward, F. Gosselin, F. Fontenay Aux Roses, Design of self-adjusting orthoses for rehabilitation, in *Proceedings of International Conference on Robotics and Applications* vol. 74 (Cambridge, MA, USA, 2009), pp. 215–223

110. K.-M. Lee, J. Guo, Kinematic and dynamic analysis of an anatomically based knee joint. J. Biomech. **43**(7), 1231–1236 (2010)

111. V.V. Patel, K. Hall, M. Ries, J. Lotz, E. Ozhinsky, C. Lindsey, Y. Lu, S. Majumdar, A three-dimensional mri analysis of knee kinematics. J. Orthop Res. **22**(2), 283–292 (2004)

112. D.-H. Wang, J. Guo, K.-M. Lee, C.-J. Yang, H. Yu, An adaptive knee joint exoskeleton based on biological geometries, in *Proceedings of IEEE International Conference on Robotics Automation* (Shanghai, China, 2011), pp. 1386–1391

113. D. Wang, K.-M. Lee, J. Guo, C.-J. Yang, Adaptive knee joint exoskeleton based on biological geometries. IEEE-ASME Trans. Mechatron. **19**(4), 1268–1278 (2014)

114. K. Ma, R. Goetz, S.K. Srivasta, Modeling of residual stress and machining distortion in aerospace components (preprint). Enterp. Soc. **9**(3), 513–516 (2010)

115. E. Diez, H. Perez, J. Marquez, A. Vizan, Feasibility study of in-process compensation of deformations in flexible milling. Int. J. Mach. Tools Manuf. **94**, 1–14 (2015)

116. M.N. Helfrick, C. Niezrecki, P. Avitabile, T. Schmidt, 3d digital image correlation methods for full-field vibration measurement. Mech. Syst. Signal Process. **25**(3), 917–927 (2011)

117. D.J. Cappelleri, G. Piazza, V. Kumar, A two dimensional vision-based force sensor for microrobotic applications. Sens. Actuat. A-Phys. **171**(2), 340–351 (2011)

118. M.Y. Tsai, C.W. Ting, C.Y. Huang, Y.S. Lai, Determination of residual strains of the emc in pbga during manufacturing and ir solder reflow processes. Microelectron. Reliab. **51**(3), 642–648 (2011)

119. I. Hanhan, E. Durnberg, G. Freihofer, P. Akin, S. Raghavan, Portable piezospectroscopy system: non-contact in-situ stress sensing through high resolution photo-luminescent mapping. J. Instrum. **9**, P11005 (2014)

120. Y. Wang, Y. Li, T. Bock, J.P. Lynch, J. Mattila, Introduction to the focused section on intelligent robotics for civil infrastructure. Int. J. Intell. Rob. Appl. **1**(3), 239–242 (2017)

121. B. Li, K. Ushiroda, L. Yang, Q. Song, J. Xiao, Wall-climbing robot for non-destructive evaluation using impact-echo and metric learning svm. Int. J. Intell. Rob. Appl. **1**(3), 255–270 (2017)

122. M. Chierichetti, M. Ruzzene, Dynamic displacement field reconstruction through a limited set of measurements: application to plates. J. Sound Vib. **331**(21), 4713–4728 (2012)

123. R. Izamshah, J.P.T. Mo, S. Ding, Hybrid deflection prediction on machining thin-wall monolithic aerospace components. Proc. Inst. Mech. Eng. Part B-J. Eng. Manuf. **226**(B4), 592–605 (2012)

124. A. Derkevorkian, S.F. Masri, J. Alvarenga, H. Boussalis, J. Bakalyar, W.L. Richards, Strain-based deformation shape-estimation algorithm for control and monitoring applications. AIAA J. **51**(9), 2231–2240 (2013)

125. P. Cerracchio, M. Gherlone, A. Tessler, Real-time displacement monitoring of a composite stiffened panel subjected to mechanical and thermal loads. Meccanica **50**(10), 2487–2496 (2015)

126. A. Tessler, J.L. Spangler, A least-squares variational method for full-field reconstruction of elastic deformations in shear-deformable plates and shells. Comput. Methods Appl Mech. Eng. **194**(2), 327–339 (2005)

127. R. Glaser, V. Caccese, M. Shahinpoor, Shape monitoring of a beam structure from measured strain or curvature. Exp. Mech. **52**(6), 591–606 (2012)

128. L.U. Odhner, A.M. Dollar, The smooth curvature model: An efficient representation of euler-bernoulli flexures as robot joints. IEEE Trans. Rob. **28**(4), 761–772 (2012)

129. R.J. Roesthuis, M. Kemp, J.J. van den Dobbelsteen, S. Misra, Three-dimensional needle shape reconstruction using an array of fiber bragg grating sensors. IEEE-ASME Trans. Mechatron. **19**(4), 1115–1126 (2014)

130. S. Laflamme, H.S. Saleem, B.K. Vasan, R.L. Geiger, D. Chen, M.R. Kessler, K. Rajan, Soft elastomeric capacitor network for strain sensing over large surfaces. IEEE-ASME Trans. Mechatron. **18**(6), 1647–1654 (2013)

131. J.-W. Park, S.-H. Sim, H.-J. Jung, Displacement estimation using multimetric data fusion. IEEE-ASME Trans. Mechatron. **18**(6), 1675–1682 (2013)

132. J. Baqersad, C. Niezrecki, P. Avitabile, Extracting full-field dynamic strain on a wind turbine rotor subjected to arbitrary excitations using 3d point tracking and a modal expansion technique. J. Sound Vib. **352**, 16–29 (2015)

133. P. Cerracchio, M. Gherlone, M. Di Sciuva, A. Tessler, A novel approach for displacement and stress monitoring of sandwich structures based on the inverse finite element method. Compos. Struct. **127**, 69–76 (2015)

134. Y. Zhao, Y. Zhao, C. Wang, S. Liang, R. Cheng, Y. Qin, P. Wang, Y. Li, X. Li, T. Hu, Design and development of a cutting force sensor based on semi-conductive strain gauge. Sens. Actuat. A-Phys. **237**, 119–127 (2016)

135. J. Guo, K. Lee, W. Liu, B. Wang, Design criteria based on modal analysis for vibration sensing of thin-wall plate machining. IEEE-ASME Trans. Mechatron. **20**(3), 1406–1417 (2015)

136. A.A.D. Sarhan, A. Matsubara, Investigation about the characterization of machine tool spindle stiffness for intelligent cnc end milling. Rob. Comput. Integr. Manuf. **34**, 133–139 (2015)

137. J.S. Bae, M.K. Kwak, D.J. Inman, Vibration suppression of a cantilever beam using eddy current damper. J. Sound Vib. **284**(3–5), 805–824 (2005)

138. J. Laborenz, M. Krack, L. Panning, J. Wallaschek, M. Denk, P.-A. Masserey, Eddy current damper for turbine blading: electromagnetic finite element analysis and measurement results. J. Eng. Gas Turbines Power **134**(4), 2012

139. J. Guo, R. Liu, K.-M. Lee, Displacement field sensing and reconstruction for vibration of a thin-wall plate, in *Proceedings of IEEE/ASME International Conference on Advanced Intelligent Mechatronics (AIM)* (Busan, Korea, 2015), pp. 1350–1355

140. J. Guo, R. Liu, K.-M. Lee, Dynamic modeling and analysis for thin-wall plate machining, in *Proceedings of the ASME Dynamic Systems and Control Conference*, vol. 3 (Columbus, Ohio, USA, 2015)

141. W. Daley, T. He, K.-M. Lee, M. Sandlin, Modeling of the natural product deboning process using biological (1999), pp. 49–54

142. M.C. Sandlin, *Model-Based Vision-Guided Automated Cutting of Natural Products* (Master, Mechanical Engineering, Georgia Institute of Technology, Atlanta, 1998)

143. T. He, *Effects of Rotor Configurations on the Characteristic Torque of a Variable-Reluctance Spherical Motor* (Ph.D., Mechanical Engineering, Georgia Institute of Technology, Atlanta, 2000)

144. K.-M. Lee, C.-K. Kwan, Design concept development of a spherical stepper for robotic. **7** (1), 175–181 (1991)

145. M.R. Claffee, *The Effects of Wing Manipulation on Automated Cutting of Biological Materials* (Master, Mechanical Engineering, Georgia Institute of Technology, Atlanta, 2006)

146. K.-M. Lee, On the development of a compliant grasping mechanism for online handling of live objects. I. Analytical model, in *Proceedings of IEEE/ASME International Conference on Advanced Intelligent Mechatronics (AIM)* (1999), pp. 354–359
147. K.-M. Lee, A.B. Webster, J. Joni, X. Yin, R. Carey, M.P. Lacy, R. Gogate, On the development of a compliant grasping mechanism for online handling of live objects. II. Design and experimental investigation, in *Proceedings of IEEE/ASME International Conference on Advanced Intelligent Mechatronics (AIM)*, (1999), pp. 360–365
148. Q. Li, K.-M. Lee, An adaptive meshless method for analyzing large mechanical deformation and contacts. J. Appl. Mech. Trans. ASME. **75**(4), 041014 (2008)

Chapter 2
Fundamentals of Mathematics

This chapter presents the mathematic fundamentals for the modeling formulation and numerical algorithm in subsequent chapters. Starting from the basics of differential geometry, the concept of curvature is introduced and the kinematics of beam and plate elements is formulated, after which the multiple shooting method is presented to solve the boundary value problems formulated in the next chapter.

2.1 Basics of Differential Geometry

Both the rotational matrix and curvature are used to describe the curved shape of a beam axis. Since only three components in a rotational matrix are independent, the rotational matrix is mutually interchangeable with a curvature vector of three components. This section shows how they are correlated and a theorem will be proved.

Given any curve in a 3D space, the moving frame $[e_1 \ e_2 \ e_3]^T$ along the axis can be expressed in the following form

$$\left\{ \begin{array}{c} \mathbf{e}_1 \\ \mathbf{e}_2 \\ \mathbf{e}_3 \end{array} \right\} = [\mathbf{R}] \left\{ \begin{array}{c} \mathbf{E}_1 \\ \mathbf{E}_2 \\ \mathbf{E}_3 \end{array} \right\} \tag{2.1}$$

where $[\mathbf{E}_1 \ \mathbf{E}_2 \ \mathbf{E}_3]^T$ is the reference frame, and $[\mathbf{R}]$ is the rotational matrix depending on the path length s. Then, taking the derivative with respect to s

$$\frac{d}{ds} \left\{ \begin{array}{c} \mathbf{e}_1 \\ \mathbf{e}_2 \\ \mathbf{e}_3 \end{array} \right\} = \frac{d[\mathbf{R}]}{ds} \left\{ \begin{array}{c} \mathbf{E}_1 \\ \mathbf{E}_2 \\ \mathbf{E}_3 \end{array} \right\} = \frac{d[\mathbf{R}]}{ds} [\mathbf{R}]^T \left\{ \begin{array}{c} \mathbf{e}_1 \\ \mathbf{e}_2 \\ \mathbf{e}_3 \end{array} \right\} \tag{2.2}$$

the curvature $\mathbf{K} = [k_1 \ k_2 \ k_3]^T$ is defined as

© Huazhong University of Science and Technology Press, Wuhan and Springer Nature Singapore Pte Ltd. 2019
J. Guo and K.-M Lee, *Flexonics for Manufacturing and Robotics*, Research on Intelligent Manufacturing, https://doi.org/10.1007/978-981-13-2667-7_2

$$skew(\mathbf{K}) = \begin{bmatrix} 0 & k_3 & -k_2 \\ -k_3 & 0 & k_1 \\ k_2 & -k_1 & 0 \end{bmatrix} = \frac{d[\mathbf{R}]}{ds}[\mathbf{R}]^{\mathrm{T}} \tag{2.3}$$

The ordinary differential equations governing $\mathbf{R}$ can be expressed in terms of $\mathbf{K}$:

$$\frac{d[\mathbf{R}]}{ds} = skew(\mathbf{K})[\mathbf{R}]^{\mathrm{T}} \tag{2.4}$$

Theorem A.1 *Given* $\mathbf{R}$ *as an rotational matrix,* $[\mathbf{A}] = \frac{d[\mathbf{R}]}{ds}[\mathbf{R}]^{\mathrm{T}}$ *is a skew matrix.*

Proof: For a rotational matrix $[\mathbf{R}]$, it satisfies the following condition

$$[\mathbf{R}][\mathbf{R}]^{\mathrm{T}} = [\mathbf{R}]^{\mathrm{T}}[\mathbf{R}] = [\mathbf{I}]$$

where $[\mathbf{I}]$ is an identity matrix.

$$\begin{aligned} [\mathbf{A}] + [\mathbf{A}]^{\mathrm{T}} &= \frac{d[\mathbf{R}]}{ds}[\mathbf{R}]^{\mathrm{T}} + [\mathbf{R}]\frac{d[\mathbf{R}]^{\mathrm{T}}}{ds} \\ &= \frac{d[\mathbf{R}][\mathbf{R}]^{\mathrm{T}}}{ds} = \frac{d[\mathbf{I}]}{ds} \\ &= 0 \end{aligned}$$

hence, $[\mathbf{A}] = -[\mathbf{A}]^{\mathrm{T}}$ is a skew matrix.

So the curvature $\mathbf{K}$ has been presented in the form of a skew matrix for the derivative of the moving frame along the path length s,

$$\frac{d}{ds}\begin{Bmatrix} \mathbf{e}_1 \\ \mathbf{e}_2 \\ \mathbf{e}_3 \end{Bmatrix} = skew(\mathbf{K})\begin{Bmatrix} \mathbf{e}_1 \\ \mathbf{e}_2 \\ \mathbf{e}_3 \end{Bmatrix} \tag{2.5}$$

It is clear that $\mathbf{K}$ is independent of what reference frame $\{\mathbf{E}_i\}$ ($i = 1, 2$ and 3) is chosen and determined by the geometry of curve via the rotational matrix in (2.3).

2.2 Curvature of a 3D Beam

As shown in Fig. 2.1, the longitudinal axis of a curved beam in the 3D space is described in a parametric form:

Fig. 2.1 A 3D curve

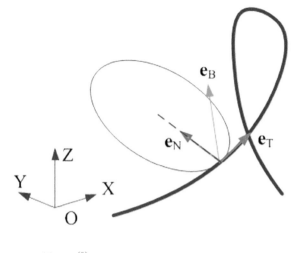

$$\mathbf{x}^{(0)} = x_i^{(0)}(t)\mathbf{E}_i \tag{2.6}$$

where t is not necessary to be the path length but any parameter ranging from t_0 to t_f.

In Fig. 2.1, $[\mathbf{e}_T, \mathbf{e}_N, \mathbf{e}_B]$ is the Frenet–Serret frame where $\mathbf{e}_T$, $\mathbf{e}_N$ and $\mathbf{e}_B$ are the tangent, normal and binormal unit vectors given in [1] as

$$\mathbf{e}_T = \frac{\dot{\mathbf{x}}^{(0)}}{\left|\dot{\mathbf{x}}^{(0)}\right|}, \mathbf{e}_N = \frac{\ddot{\mathbf{x}}^{(0)}}{\left|\ddot{\mathbf{x}}^{(0)}\right|}, \mathbf{e}_B = \mathbf{e}_T \times \mathbf{e}_N \tag{2.7}$$

where "$\cdot$" denotes the derivate with respect to t.

The Frenet–Serret formula is provided as:

$$\frac{d}{ds}\left\{\begin{array}{c}\mathbf{e}_T\\\mathbf{e}_N\\\mathbf{e}_B\end{array}\right\} = \begin{bmatrix}0 & \kappa & 0\\-\kappa & 0 & \tau\\0 & -\tau & 0\end{bmatrix}\left\{\begin{array}{c}\mathbf{e}_T\\\mathbf{e}_N\\\mathbf{e}_B\end{array}\right\} \tag{2.8}$$

where the path length s can be calculated as a function of t

$$s = \int_{t_0}^{t} \sqrt{\dot{x}_1^{(0)2} + \dot{x}_2^{(0)2} + \dot{x}_3^{(0)2}}\,dt \tag{2.9}$$

So the overall length of the curve can be obtained as

$$L = s(t_f) = \int_{t_0}^{t_f} \sqrt{\dot{x}_1^{(0)2} + \dot{x}_2^{(0)2} + \dot{x}_3^{(0)2}}\,dt \tag{2.10}$$

And the curvature κ and torsion τ are given by

$$\kappa = \frac{\left|\dot{\mathbf{x}}^{(0)} \times \ddot{\mathbf{x}}^{(0)}\right|}{\left|\dot{\mathbf{x}}^{(0)}\right|^3} \tag{2.11a}$$

$$\tau = \frac{\dot{\mathbf{x}}^{(0)} \cdot (\ddot{\mathbf{x}}^{(0)} \times \dddot{\mathbf{x}}^{(0)})}{\left|\dot{\mathbf{x}}^{(0)} \times \ddot{\mathbf{x}}^{(0)}\right|^2} \tag{2.11b}$$

It is noted that $\mathbf{e}_1^{(0)}$ and $\mathbf{e}_T$ are the same unit tangent vector, while $\mathbf{e}_2^{(0)}$ and $\mathbf{e}_N$, $\mathbf{e}_3^{(0)}$ and $\mathbf{e}_B$ are not necessarily the same. Because based on the definition, $\mathbf{e}_2^{(0)}$ and $\mathbf{e}_3^{(0)}$ are defined by the shape of the beam cross section while $\mathbf{e}_N$ and $\mathbf{e}_B$ are defined by the axial curve shape as indicated in (2.7). These two frames are related by a pure rotation

$$\left\{ \begin{array}{c} \mathbf{e}_T \\ \mathbf{e}_N \\ \mathbf{e}_B \end{array} \right\} = \left[\mathbf{R}_\varphi^{(0)} \right] \left\{ \begin{array}{c} \mathbf{e}_1^{(0)} \\ \mathbf{e}_2^{(0)} \\ \mathbf{e}_3^{(0)} \end{array} \right\} \quad \text{where} \quad \left[\mathbf{R}_\varphi^{(0)} \right] = \left[\begin{array}{ccc} 1 & 0 & 0 \\ 0 & \cos \varphi^{(0)} & \sin \varphi^{(0)} \\ 0 & -\sin \varphi^{(0)} & \cos \varphi^{(0)} \end{array} \right] \tag{2.12}$$

Assuming $\varphi^{(0)}$ is constant and $\mathbf{e}_i^{(0)}$ coincides with $\mathbf{E}_i$ ($i = 1, 2$ and 3) at the base ($s = 0$), then

$$\cos \varphi^{(0)} = \mathbf{E}_2 \cdot \mathbf{e}_N|_{s=0}, \quad \sin \varphi^{(0)} = \mathbf{E}_3 \cdot \mathbf{e}_N|_{s=0} \tag{2.13}$$

Differentiating (2.12) and combining with (2.8), one can arrive at

$$\frac{d}{ds} \left\{ \begin{array}{c} \mathbf{e}_1^{(0)} \\ \mathbf{e}_2^{(0)} \\ \mathbf{e}_3^{(0)} \end{array} \right\} = \left[\mathbf{R}_\varphi^{(0)} \right]^T \frac{d}{ds} \left\{ \begin{array}{c} \mathbf{e}_T \\ \mathbf{e}_N \\ \mathbf{e}_B \end{array} \right\} = \left[\mathbf{R}_\varphi^{(0)} \right]^T \left[\begin{array}{ccc} 0 & \kappa & 0 \\ -\kappa & 0 & \tau \\ 0 & -\tau & 0 \end{array} \right] \left[\mathbf{R}_\varphi^{(0)} \right] \left\{ \begin{array}{c} \mathbf{e}_1^{(0)} \\ \mathbf{e}_2^{(0)} \\ \mathbf{e}_3^{(0)} \end{array} \right\}$$

Similar to (2.5), the initial frame $\left[\mathbf{e}_1^{(0)}, \mathbf{e}_2^{(0)}, \mathbf{e}_3^{(0)} \right]^T$ satisfies

$$\frac{d}{ds} \left\{ \begin{array}{c} \mathbf{e}_1^{(0)} \\ \mathbf{e}_2^{(0)} \\ \mathbf{e}_3^{(0)} \end{array} \right\} = skew(\mathbf{K}^{(0)}) \left\{ \begin{array}{c} \mathbf{e}_1^{(0)} \\ \mathbf{e}_2^{(0)} \\ \mathbf{e}_3^{(0)} \end{array} \right\}$$

$$\text{where } skew(\mathbf{K}^{(0)}) = \left[\begin{array}{ccc} 0 & k_3^{(0)} & -k_2^{(0)} \\ -k_3^{(0)} & 0 & k_1^{(0)} \\ k_2^{(0)} & -k_1^{(0)} & 0 \end{array} \right].$$

Comparing the above relations, components of the initial curvature $\mathbf{K}^{(0)}$ are given as

$$k_1^{(0)} = \tau, \quad k_2^{(0)} = \kappa \sin \varphi^{(0)}, \quad k_3^{(0)} = \kappa \cos \varphi^{(0)} \tag{2.14}$$

Here $\varphi^{(0)}$ is a constant, while κ and τ as functions of s can be interpolated using polynomials.

2.3 Kinematics of a 3D Beam

The forward procedure is presented in the previous section to obtain $\mathbf{K}^{(0)}$ from the initial beam shape, and this section focuses on the inverse process to obtain the nodal coordinate along the beam axis from the calculated deformed curvature $\mathbf{K}$.

The deformed curved beam axis is given by

$$\mathbf{x} = x_i \mathbf{E}_i \tag{2.15}$$

where x_i ($i = 1, 2$ and 3) are the nodal coordinates. It is noted that differentiation of (2.15) will give the tangential direction

$$\frac{d\mathbf{x}}{ds} = \frac{dx_i \mathbf{E}_i}{ds} = \frac{dx_i}{ds}\mathbf{E}_i = (1+\varepsilon)\mathbf{e}_1 = (1+\varepsilon)R_{1i}\mathbf{E}_i$$

hence

$$\frac{dx_i}{ds} = (1+\varepsilon)R_{1i} \tag{2.16}$$

where ε is the longitudinal strain to be discussed in Sect. 3.2. Recall that only the first row of $\mathbf{R}$ is involved in the nodal coordinates along the beam axis; and the angle φ determines the relative twisting of the beam cross section with respect to the axis. In other words, they completely determine the deformed beam shape, so it is the next task to find $[R_{11} \ R_{12} \ R_{13}]$ and φ from $\mathbf{K}$.

As shown in (2.5), the moving frame along the beam axis satisfies

$$\frac{d}{ds}\mathbf{e}_i = skew(\mathbf{K})_{ij}\mathbf{e}_j \tag{2.17}$$

where

$$skew(\mathbf{K})_{ij} = \frac{dR_{ik}}{ds}R_{kj}^T \tag{2.18}$$

As discussed in Sect. 2.1, the deformed beam shape can be obtained once the rotational matrix $[\mathbf{R}]$ is determined. Referring to [2], $[\mathbf{R}]$ can be completely determined by its first row of $[\mathbf{R}]_1 = [R_{11}\ R_{12}\ R_{13}]$ and the twisting angle φ,

$$
\mathbf{R} = \begin{bmatrix} R_{11} & R_{12} & R_{13} \\ R_{21} & R_{22} & R_{23} \\ R_{31} & R_{32} & R_{33} \end{bmatrix}
$$

$$
= \begin{bmatrix} 1 & 0 & 0 \\ 0 & \cos\varphi & \sin\varphi \\ 0 & -\sin\varphi & \cos\varphi \end{bmatrix} \begin{bmatrix} R_{11} & R_{12} & R_{13} \\ -R_{12} & 1 - R_{12}^2/(1+R_{11}) & -R_{12}R_{13}/(1+R_{11}) \\ -R_{13} & -R_{12}R_{13}/(1+R_{11}) & 1 - R_{13}^2/(1+R_{11}) \end{bmatrix}
$$

$$\tag{2.19}$$

From (2.17), k_1 can be expressed as following:

$$
k_1 = \mathbf{e}_3 \cdot \frac{\mathrm{d}\mathbf{e}_2}{\mathrm{d}s}
$$

Substituting (2.1), (2.17), (2.18) and (2.19), and also considering $R_{11}^2 + R_{12}^2 + R_{13}^2 = 1$, the above equation can be rewritten as

$$
\frac{\mathrm{d}\varphi}{\mathrm{d}s} = k_1 - k_2 \frac{R_{12}\cos\varphi + R_{13}\sin\varphi}{1 + R_{11}} - k_3 \frac{R_{13}\cos\varphi - R_{12}\sin\varphi}{1 + R_{11}} \tag{2.20}
$$

From (2.4), the first row of $\mathbf{R}$ is readily expressed as

$$
\frac{\mathrm{d}R_{1j}}{\mathrm{d}s} = skew(\mathbf{K})_{1k}R_{kj} \tag{2.21}
$$

Grouping (2.16), (2.20) and (2.21), the kinematics of a 3D beam is governed by

$$
R'_{11} = k_3 R_{21} - k_2 R_{31} \tag{2.22a}
$$

$$
R'_{12} = k_3 R_{22} - k_2 R_{32} \tag{2.22b}
$$

$$
R'_{13} = k_3 R_{23} - k_2 R_{33} \tag{2.22c}
$$

$$
\varphi' = k_1 + k_2 \frac{R_{13}R_{32} - R_{12}R_{33}}{1 + R_{11}} + k_3 \frac{R_{12}R_{23} - R_{13}R_{22}}{1 + R_{11}} \tag{2.22d}
$$

$$
x'_1 = (1 + \varepsilon)R_{11} \tag{2.22e}
$$

$$x_2' = (1+\varepsilon)R_{12} \qquad\qquad (2.22\text{f})$$

$$x_3' = (1+\varepsilon)R_{13} \qquad\qquad (2.22\text{g})$$

where $'$ denotes derivative with respect to the path length s.

The formulation is best illustrated with numerical examples with loading-free conditions to verify the kinematic analysis. So, the curve shape is not deformed

$$\mathbf{K} = \mathbf{K}^{(0)} \text{ and } \varepsilon = 0$$

The following procedure will be adopted.

(1) Given a parametric relation (2.6) of a beam axial curve, determine the curvature (2.14) as a function of the path length.
(2) Reconstruct the original beam shape $\mathbf{x}^{(0)}$ by numerically solving the IVP of (2.22) with initial conditions at $s = 0$: $R_{11} = 1, R_{12} = R_{13} = 0;\ \varphi = 0;\ x_1 = x_2 = x_3 = 0$
(3) Compare the calculated curve shape $\mathbf{x}$ with the original shape $\mathbf{x}^{(0)}$.

Three examples are chosen to illustrate the curvature description of beam geometry. The first example is a planar curved beam with a non-constant curvature κ and zero torsion τ. The next example illustrates the case of constant κ and τ using a helix curved beam, where the principal axes are not aligned with the global reference frame at the base. The final example shows the case of non-constant κ and τ with a general 3D curved beam.

Example 2.3.1 Planar Curved Beam.
Consider a curved beam on the XY plane with the axial curve described as

$$x_1^{(0)} = 10 \sin t, \ x_2^{(0)} = 5 - 5 \cos t, \ x_3^{(0)} = 0$$

For $t \in [0 \quad 2\pi]$, the overall curve length given by (2.10) is $L = 48.44$.
As shown in Fig. 2.2a, there is only one non-zero component of curvature, κ, for a planar curve. Given the highly nonlinear relation between κ and s, a polynomial of s is employed to approximate κ. Percentage errors for the approximated curvature and the reconstructed beam shape $\mathbf{x}$ are calculated as

$$e_\kappa = \frac{\max|\kappa - \kappa_{approx.}|}{\kappa} \times 100\%$$

$$e_{beam} = \frac{\left|\mathbf{x} - \mathbf{x}^{(0)}\right|_{s=L}}{L} \times 100\%$$

Fig. 2.2 Verification with a planar curve (non-constant curvature)

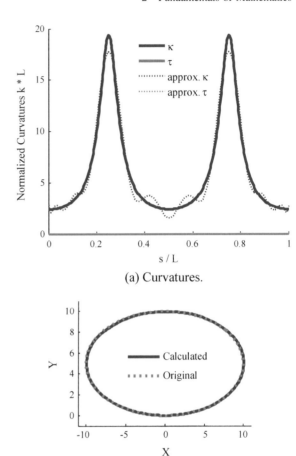

(a) Curvatures.

(b) Comparison of the original and calculated curves.

Because the calculation error accumulates through the integration, it is expected that the reconstructed beam shape has maximum error at the end $s = L$, where in this example, $e_\kappa = 8.38\%$ and $e_{beam} = 0.025\%$. Although there is obvious deviation between the polynomial approximation and the true value of κ, the elliptic shape can still be reconstructed as shown in Fig. 2.2b.

Example 2.3.2 A Helix Curved Beam.

For a helix curve with a radius of r and pitch of $2\pi p$, its parametric expression can be written as

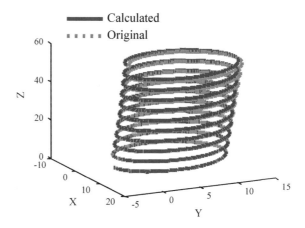

Fig. 2.3 Verification with a helix curve (constant curvature)

$$x = r \sin t, \; y = r - r \cos t, \; z = pt$$

In order to orient the global reference frame to the Frenet–Serret frame at the helix base, it requires a rigid body rotation

$$
\begin{Bmatrix} x_1^{(0)} \\ x_2^{(0)} \\ x_3^{(0)} \end{Bmatrix} =
\begin{bmatrix} \cos \beta & 0 & \sin \beta \\ 0 & 1 & 0 \\ -\sin \beta & 0 & \cos \beta \end{bmatrix}
\begin{Bmatrix} x \\ y \\ z \end{Bmatrix}
\quad \text{where } \beta = \tan^{-1} \frac{p}{r}
$$

Employing (2.11), it can be obtained that

$$
\kappa = \frac{r}{r^2 + p^2} \quad \text{and} \quad \tau = \frac{p}{r^2 + p^2}
$$

when $r = 7.239$ mm and $p = 5.715$ mm, the curvatures are calculated as $\kappa = 0.0851$ mm^{-1} and $\tau = 0.0672$ mm^{-1}. Figure 2.3 shows the simulated result of the helix curve with 10 pitches $(t \in [0 \quad 20\pi])$ where the percentage error e_{beam} is 2.83%.

Example 2.3.3 A 3D Curved Beam.
   The last example is given by

$$
x_1^{(0)} = 25 \sin t, \quad x_2^{(0)} = 10 - 10 \cos 2t, \quad x_3^{(0)} = 20 - 20 \cos 3t
$$

For $t \in [0 \quad \pi/2]$, the overall curve length given by (2.10) is $L = 71.973$.
   For illustration, the beam cross-section aspect ratio is set to be 5:2 and its snap shots are shown along the longitudinal axis. As shown in Fig. 2.4a, both κ and τ are nonlinear functions of s. Although the error e_κ in the curvature approximation is as large as 23.22%, the error in the reconstructed beam shape is obtained as $e_{\text{beam}} = 0.71\%$. In Fig. 2.4b, the Frenet–Serret frame is also shown at the base and tip of

Fig. 2.4 Verification with a 3D curve with non-constant curvatures

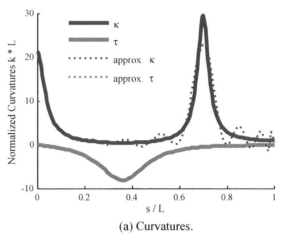

(a) Curvatures.

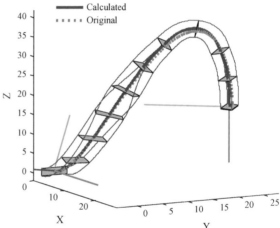

(b) Comparison of the original and calculated curves.

the curved beam with $\mathbf{e}_T$, $\mathbf{e}_N$ and $\mathbf{e}_B$ being denoted in red, green and blue, respectively. From (2.7), $\mathbf{e}_N$ and $\mathbf{e}_B$ can be obtained as following:

$$\mathbf{e}_N = \begin{bmatrix} 0 & 0.2169 & 0.9762 \end{bmatrix}^{\mathrm{T}}, \ \mathbf{e}_B = \begin{bmatrix} 0 & -0.9762 & 0.2169 \end{bmatrix}^{\mathrm{T}}$$

So they do not necessarily coincide with the cross section principal axes $\mathbf{e}_2^{(0)}$ and $\mathbf{e}_3^{(0)}$.

Fig. 2.5 An element in a
compliant plate

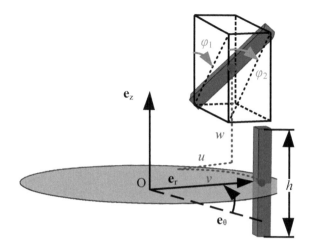

2.4   Kinematics of an Annular Plate

This section provides a kinematic analysis of thin annular plate deformations, where
the relation between the displacements and strains of a plate element is formulated.
As shown in Fig. 2.5, a cylindrical reference frame $[\mathbf{e}_r \; \mathbf{e}_\theta \; \mathbf{e}_z]$ locates at the center
point O of a compliant plate, where $\mathbf{e}_r$ and $\mathbf{e}_\theta$ are curvilinear axes on the referenced
mid-surface, and $\mathbf{e}_z$ is normal to the mid-surface. An element of thickness h is
shown to displace by $u\mathbf{e}_r + v\mathbf{e}_\theta + w\mathbf{e}_z$, and orient by φ_1 around $\mathbf{e}_r$ and φ_2 around $\mathbf{e}_\theta$.
Then the displacement of any point on the element ($-h/2 \le z \le h/2$) is obtained
as

$$\mathbf{D} = (u + z \sin \varphi_2)\mathbf{e}_r + (v - z \sin \varphi_1)\mathbf{e}_\theta + w\mathbf{e}_z \qquad (2.23)$$

For small rotations, $\sin \varphi_1 \simeq \varphi_1 \simeq -\frac{\partial w}{r\partial \theta}$ and $\sin \varphi_2 \simeq \varphi_2 \simeq \frac{\partial w}{\partial r}$, (2.23) is
rewritten as

$$\mathbf{D} = (u - z\frac{\partial w}{\partial r})\mathbf{e}_r + (v - z\frac{\partial w}{r\partial \theta})\mathbf{e}_\theta + w\mathbf{e}_z \qquad (2.24)$$

In a general case where strains are nonlinear, the displacement can be expressed as

$$\mathbf{D} = u_1\mathbf{e}_r + u_2\mathbf{e}_\theta + u_3\mathbf{e}_z$$

where $u_1 = u - z\frac{\partial w}{\partial r}$, $u_2 = v - z\frac{\partial w}{r\partial \theta}$, $u_3 = w$. Then the displacement gradient is
obtained as

$$\frac{\partial \mathbf{D}}{\partial r} = \frac{\partial u_1}{\partial r}\mathbf{e}_r + \frac{\partial u_2}{\partial r}\mathbf{e}_\theta + \frac{\partial u_3}{\partial r}\mathbf{e}_z$$

$$\frac{\partial \mathbf{D}}{r\partial \theta} = (\frac{\partial u_1}{r\partial \theta} - \frac{u_2}{r})\mathbf{e}_r + (\frac{u_1}{r} + \frac{\partial u_2}{r\partial \theta})\mathbf{e}_\theta + \frac{\partial u_3}{r\partial \theta}\mathbf{e}_z \qquad (2.25)$$

$$\frac{\partial \mathbf{D}}{\partial z} = \frac{\partial u_1}{\partial z}\mathbf{e}_r + \frac{\partial u_2}{\partial z}\mathbf{e}_\theta + \frac{\partial u_3}{\partial z}\mathbf{e}_z$$

The gradient of the displacement is calculated as

$$\nabla \mathbf{D} = \frac{\partial \mathbf{D}}{\partial r}\mathbf{e}_r + \frac{\partial \mathbf{D}}{r\partial \theta}\mathbf{e}_\theta + \frac{\partial \mathbf{D}}{\partial z}\mathbf{e}_z = \begin{bmatrix} \frac{\partial u_1}{\partial r} & \frac{\partial u_1}{r\partial \theta} - \frac{u_2}{r} & \frac{\partial u_1}{\partial z} \\ \frac{\partial u_2}{\partial r} & \frac{u_1}{r} + \frac{\partial u_2}{r\partial \theta} & \frac{\partial u_2}{\partial z} \\ \frac{\partial u_3}{\partial r} & \frac{\partial u_3}{r\partial \theta} & \frac{\partial u_3}{\partial z} \end{bmatrix} \qquad (2.26)$$

Substitute (2.30) into the following strain tensor

$$\mathbf{E} = \frac{1}{2}[\nabla \mathbf{D} + (\nabla \mathbf{D})^T + (\nabla \mathbf{D})^T \nabla \mathbf{D}]$$

Its components are given as

$$\varepsilon_{rr} = \frac{1}{2}(2u_{1,r} + u_{1,r}^2 + u_{2,r}^2 + u_{3,r}^2)$$

$$\varepsilon_{\theta\theta} = \frac{1}{2r^2}(u_1^2 + u_2^2 - 2u_2 u_{1,\theta} + u_{1,\theta}^2 + 2ru_{2,\theta} + u_{2,\theta}^2 + 2u_1(r + u_{2,\theta}) + u_{3,\theta}^2)$$

$$\varepsilon_{zz} = u_{3,z} + \frac{1}{2}(u_{1,z}^2 + u_{2,z}^2 + u_{3,z}^2)$$

$$\varepsilon_{r\theta} = \frac{1}{2r}(-u_2(1 + u_{1,r}) + u_{1,\theta}(1 + u_{1,r}) + ru_{2,r} + u_1 u_{2,r} + u_{2,\theta}u_{2,r} + u_{3,\theta}u_{3,r})$$

$$\varepsilon_{rz} = \frac{1}{2}(u_{1,z}(1 + u_{1,r}) + u_{2,z}u_{2,r} + (1 + u_{3,z})u_{3,r})$$

$$\varepsilon_{\theta z} = \frac{1}{2r}(-u_2 u_{1,z} + u_{1,z}u_{1,\theta} + u_{2,z}(r + u_1 + u_{2,\theta}) + u_{3,\theta} + u_{3,z}u_{3,\theta})$$

Considering

$$u_1 = u - z\frac{\partial w}{\partial r}, \ u_2 = v - z\frac{\partial w}{r\partial\theta}, \ u_3 = w \qquad (2.27)$$

the above strains are given by

$$\varepsilon_{rr} = \frac{1}{2}(2u_r + w_r^2 + (\frac{zw_\theta}{r^2} + v_r - \frac{zw_{r\theta}}{r})^2 - 2zw_{rr} + (u_r - zw_{rr})^2)$$

$$\varepsilon_{\theta\theta} = \frac{1}{2r^4}(r^2w_\theta^2 + 2r^2(rv_\theta - zw_{\theta\theta}) + 2r^3(u - zw_r)$$
$$+ \cdots (ru + rv_\theta - z(w_{\theta\theta} + rw_r))^2 + (rv - ru_\theta - zw_\theta + rzw_{r\theta})^2)$$

$$\varepsilon_{zz} = \frac{1}{2}(2w_z + w_z^2 + \frac{(-rv_z + w_\theta + zw_{\theta z})^2}{r^2} + (-u_z + w_r + zw_{rz})^2)$$

$$\varepsilon_{r\theta} = \frac{1}{2}(\frac{zw_\theta}{r^2} + \frac{-rv + zw_\theta}{r^2} + v_r + \frac{w_\theta w_r}{r} - \frac{zw_{r\theta}}{r} + \frac{u_\theta - zw_{r\theta}}{r}$$
$$+ \cdots \frac{1}{r^4}(ru + rv_\theta - z(w_{\theta\theta} + rw_r))(zw_\theta + r(rv_r - zw_{r\theta}))$$
$$+ \cdots \frac{1}{r^2}(rv - ru_\theta - zw_\theta + rzw_{r\theta})(-u_r + zw_{rr}))$$

$$\varepsilon_{rz} = \frac{1}{2}(u_z + w_z w_r - zw_{rz} + \frac{1}{r^3}(rv_z - w_\theta - zw_{\theta z})(zw_\theta + r(rv_r - zw_{r\theta}))$$
$$+ \cdots (u_z - w_r - zw_{rz})(u_r - zw_{rr}))$$

$$\varepsilon_{\theta z} = \frac{1}{2}(v_z + \frac{w_z w_\theta}{r} - \frac{zw_{\theta z}}{r} - \frac{1}{r^3}(rv_z - w_\theta - zw_{\theta z})(-ru - rv_\theta + z(w_{\theta\theta} + rw_r))$$
$$- \cdots \frac{1}{r^2}(u_z - w_r - zw_{rz})(rv - ru_\theta - zw_\theta + rzw_{r\theta}))$$

For a thin-wall plate where in-plane deformations are small compared to the out-of-plane displacement. Neglecting all higher order terms except for those involving w, the relation between the strains and displacement can be obtained as

Fig. 2.6 Multiple shooting
method

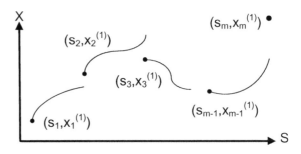

Fig. 2.6 Multiple shooting
method

$$\varepsilon_{rr} = \frac{1}{2}\left(2u_r + w_r^2 - 2zw_{rr}\right)$$

$$\varepsilon_{\theta\theta} = \frac{1}{2r^4}\left(r^2 w_\theta^2 + 2r^2\left(rv_\theta - zw_{\theta\theta}\right) + 2r^3\left(u - zw_r\right)\right)$$

$$\varepsilon_{zz} = \frac{1}{2}\left(2w_z + w_z^2\right)$$

$$\varepsilon_{r\theta} = \frac{1}{2}\left(\frac{2zw_\theta}{r^2} - \frac{v}{r} + v_r + \frac{w_\theta w_r}{r} - \frac{2zw_{r\theta}}{r} + \frac{u_\theta}{r}\right)$$

$$\varepsilon_{rz} = \frac{1}{2}\left(u_z + w_z w_r - zw_{rz}\right)$$

$$\varepsilon_{\theta z} = \frac{1}{2}\left(v_z + \frac{w_z w_\theta}{r} - \frac{zw_{\theta z}}{r}\right)$$

$$(2.28)$$

2.5 Multiple Shooting Method

The boundary value problem (BVP) of a compliant beam or plate can be written in
the following form:

$$\mathbf{X}' = \mathbf{f}(s, \mathbf{X}), \quad \mathbf{g}(\mathbf{X}(0), \mathbf{X}(1)) = \mathbf{0} \tag{2.29}$$

where $\mathbf{X}$ is a vector of the system variables; $0 \le s \le 1$; and g(·) is the boundary
conditions specifying the geometrical loading constraints at both ends. The BVP
(2.29) is recast as an IVP and solved using a MSM [3, 4]. For this, the region [0,
1] is divided into $m - 1$ sections by m nodes as shown in Fig. 2.6, where s_i is the arc
length from the root to the ith node; $x_i^{(n)}$ is the initial guesses for the ith section, and
the superscript (n) denotes the nth guess.

The BVP can then be posed as a set of m first-order non-linear equations (2.30)
subjected to a set of m constraints (2.31) as functions of the initial guesses:

$$\mathbf{X}' = \mathbf{f}(s, \mathbf{X}), \quad \mathbf{X}(s_i) = \mathbf{x}_i^{(n)} \tag{2.30}$$

$$\mathbf{C}(\mathbf{x}^{(n)}) := \begin{bmatrix} \mathbf{C}_1(\mathbf{x}_1^{(n)}, \mathbf{x}_2^{(n)}) \\ \vdots \\ \mathbf{C}_{m-1}(\mathbf{x}_{m-1}^{(n)}, \mathbf{x}_m^{(n)}) \\ \mathbf{C}_m(\mathbf{x}_1^{(n)}, \mathbf{x}_m^{(n)}) \end{bmatrix} := \begin{bmatrix} \mathbf{X}(s_2; s_1, \mathbf{x}_1^{(n)}) - \mathbf{x}_2^{(n)} \\ \vdots \\ \mathbf{X}(s_m; s_{m-1}, \mathbf{x}_{m-1}^{(n)}) - \mathbf{x}_m^{(n)} \\ \mathbf{g}(\mathbf{x}_1^{(n)}, \mathbf{x}_m^{(n)}) \end{bmatrix} \tag{2.31}$$

Using the Newton method, the initial guesses are updated using (2.32):

$$\mathbf{x}^{(n+1)} = \mathbf{x}^{(n)} - \alpha \left[D\mathbf{C}(\mathbf{x}^{(n)}) \right]^{-1} \mathbf{C}(\mathbf{x}^{(n)}), \quad n = 0, 1, \dots \tag{2.32}$$

where $DC = \partial \mathbf{C}/\partial \mathbf{x}^{(n)}$ is a matrix, α is a coefficient for the iteration step size. The iteration process of (2.32) stops until the magnitude of $\mathbf{C}(\mathbf{x}^{(n)})$ is smaller than the tolerance error Err_{tol}, implying that the solution is continuous and satisfies the boundary conditions. The MSM can be implemented using the following steps:

(1) Set the initial guess $\mathbf{x}^{(0)} = [\mathbf{x}_1^{(0)} \quad \mathbf{x}_2^{(0)} \quad \cdots \quad \mathbf{x}_m^{(0)}]$.
(2) Solve the IVP with $\mathbf{X}(0) = \mathbf{x}^{(0)}$.
(3) Calculate the residual $\|\mathbf{C}(\mathbf{x}^{(0)})\|$ and corresponding $DC = \partial \mathbf{C}/\partial \mathbf{x}^{(0)}$.
(4) Update the initial guess by (2.32).
(5) Repeat steps 2–4 (replacing $\mathbf{x}^{(0)}$ with $\mathbf{x}^{(n)}$) until $\|\mathbf{C}(\mathbf{x}^{(n)})\| <$ tolerance error Err_{tol}.

2.6 Summary

This chapter has presented the mathematical fundamentals for the subsequent chapters, where differential geometry is the most critical part in formulating the flexible beam and plate models. The multiple shooting method is the numerical method employed to solve the formulated boundary value problems throughout this book.

References

1. H.W. Guggenheimer, *Differential Geometry* (Dover Publications, New York, 1977)
2. P.F. Pai, A.N. Palazotto, Large-deformation analysis of flexible beams. Int. J. Solids Struct. **33** (9), 1335–1353 (1996)
3. H.B. Keller, *Numerical Methods for Two-Point Boundary-Value Problems* (Waltham, Massachusetts, Blaisdell, 1968)
4. J. Stoer, R. Bulirsch, *Introduction to Numerical Analysis* (Springer, New York, 1993)

Chapter 3
Flexible Elements

This chapter formulates the boundary value problems for the flexible elements of beam and plate structures, where the beam deformations are captured in the 2D and 3D spaces and the plate deformations are modeled in the 3D space. Two common assumptions are employed: (1) the material is isotropic, homogeneous and linear elastic. (2) Cross sections remain planar and normal to the reference axis before and after deformations. Then the boundary value problems can be written in a compact form,

$$\mathbf{X}' = \mathbf{f}(t, \mathbf{X}(t)), \ \mathbf{g}(\mathbf{X}(t_1), \mathbf{X}(t_2)) = \mathbf{0} \qquad (3.1a, b)$$

where t is the independent variable, $\mathbf{X}$ is the vector of state variables, $\mathbf{f}(\cdot)$ is a nonlinear function characterizes the governing relation, $\mathbf{g}(\cdot)$ specifies the motion and/or loading constraints on the boundaries $t = t_1$ and $t = t_2$.

To further relax common assumptions in traditional boundary constraints on the flexible elements, a generalized constraint referred as the bio-joint model is formulated to emulate a natural biological joint which is featured with multi-axis rotation.

3.1 Two-Dimensional Beam

The Euler–Bernoulli beam theory is adopted to formulate the flexible-beam model to capture the 2D large deformations due to external forces, moments and constraints; both point and distributed external loadings are considered.

In Fig. 3.1, the local coordinate frames, "xyz" and "$\xi\eta\zeta$" (each with a subscript indicating its location along the beam path-length), are defined in the un-deformed and deformed configurations respectively. For examples, $x_0y_0z_0$ and $x_1y_1z_1$ are the local coordinate frames at P_0 and P_1 in the undeformed configuration, respectively. Similarly, $P_s(x_s, y_s, z_s)$ and $Q_s(\xi_s, \eta_s, \zeta_s)$ represent the same material point to describe the beam shapes before and after deformation, respectively, where the

© Huazhong University of Science and Technology Press, Wuhan and Springer Nature Singapore Pte Ltd. 2019
J. Guo and K.-M Lee, *Flexonics for Manufacturing and Robotics*, Research on Intelligent Manufacturing, https://doi.org/10.1007/978-981-13-2667-7_3

Fig. 3.1 Two-dimensional deformations of a flexible beam

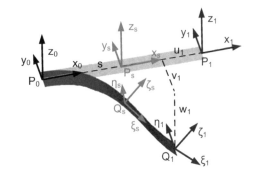

Fig. 3.2 Formulation of a beam model

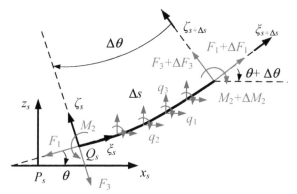

(a) Force and moment equilibrium.

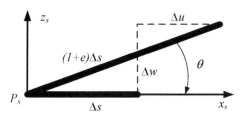

(b) Displacements and orientation relations.

subscript s denotes the path-length normalized to the beam length L; and u_s, v_s and w_s are the nodal displacements along x_s, y_s and z_s axis directions, respectively. All coordinates follow the right-hand rule with x_s and ξ_s assigned along the neutral axis of the beam, and z_s and ζ_s normal to the beam surface.

As an illustration, consider an element with length Δs in a compliant beam shown in Fig. 3.2a. The element is subjected to two concentrated loads (F_1 and F_3) and a moment (M_2) as well as two external distributed loads (q_1 and q_3) and distributed moment (q_2), where the subscripts 1, 2 or 3 corresponds to the x, y or z (ξ, η or ζ) direction respectively. In Fig. 3.2a, the concentrated loads and moment are presented in the deformed coordinates, $\xi_s \eta_s \zeta_s$; the external distributed loads and moment are in the undeformed coordinates, $x_s y_s z_s$; and θ is the slope of the deformed beam shape.

Based on static analysis of a beam element, the equations for the force and moment equilibrium are given by (3.2a–c):

$$-F_1 + (F_1 + \Delta F_1)\cos \Delta\theta + (F_3 + \Delta F_3)\sin \Delta\theta + q_1 \Delta s \cos \theta - q_3 \Delta s \sin \theta = 0 \tag{3.2a}$$

$$-F_3 + (F_3 + \Delta F_3)\cos \Delta\theta - (F_1 + \Delta F_1)\sin \Delta\theta + q_1 \Delta s \sin \theta + q_3 \Delta s \cos \theta = 0 \tag{3.2b}$$

$$-M_2 + M_2 + \Delta M_2 - (1+e)\Delta s(F_3 + \Delta F_3) + q_1 \Delta s^2/2 - q_3 \Delta s^2/2 + q_2 \Delta s = 0 \tag{3.2c}$$

where e is the axial strain. For an infinitesimally small Δs, $\sin\Delta\theta \approx \Delta\theta$ and $\cos\Delta\theta \approx 1$; then (3.2) can be rewritten in a differential form by neglecting the higher order terms, where the prime denotes derivative with respect to s:

$$F_1' = -F_3 \theta' - q_1 \cos \theta + q_3 \sin \theta \tag{3.3a}$$

$$F_3' = F_1 \theta' - q_1 \sin \theta - q_3 \cos \theta \tag{3.3b}$$

$$M_2' = (1+e)F_3 - q_2 \tag{3.3c}$$

The element displaces as well as deforms as illustrated in Fig. 3.2b, where Δs and $[(1+e)\Delta s]$ are the original and deformed element lengths, respectively. From Fig. 3.2b, the nodal displacements and orientation can be obtained as follows:

$$\frac{\Delta s + \Delta u}{(1+e)\Delta s} = \cos \theta \quad \text{and} \quad \frac{\Delta w}{(1+e)\Delta s} = -\sin \theta$$

These aforementioned relations can be rewritten in differential forms as follows:

$$u' = (1+e)\cos \theta - 1 \tag{3.4a}$$

$$w' = -(1+e)\sin \theta \tag{3.4b}$$

Denoting

$$\theta' = \rho_2 \tag{3.4c}$$

(3.3) can be recast as follows:

$$F_1' = -F_3\rho_2 - q_1 \cos\theta + q_3 \sin\theta \tag{3.4d}$$

$$F_3' = F_1\rho_2 - q_1 \sin\theta - q_3 \cos\theta \tag{3.4e}$$

$$M_2' = (1+e)F_3 - q_2 \tag{3.4f}$$

where e and ρ_2 are given by

$$e = \frac{F_1}{EA} \text{ and } \rho_2 = \frac{M_2}{EI} \tag{3.5a, b}$$

In (3.5), E is the elastic modulus, A is the cross-section area, and I is the moment of inertia. In addition, the axial strain on the upper surface is given by

$$\varepsilon_{11} = e - \rho_2 h/2 \tag{3.6a, b}$$

where h is the beam thickness.

Appropriate boundary conditions must be specified to solve (3.4) for the six unknowns $[u, w, \theta, F_1, F_3, M_2]^T$. Table 3.1 summarizes four typical boundary conditions, which are also commonly specified for analyzing columns. For a cantilever (type 1), where the slope and displacements are zeros at the fixed end, the forces and moment at the free end must be specified. For a beam with both ends constrained with pin joints (type 2), the displacement constraints cannot sustain any moment; $M_2 = 0$ but F_1 must be specified. As will be illustrated in Chap. 4, type 3 and type 4 are specified for a flexible robot designed for sensor attachment and corner negotiation. Type 3 is similar to type 2, but can resist nonzero moments while maintaining zero slopes at both ends. In type 4, a nonzero moment can be exerted against an offset pinned end. Unlike buckling analyses, where the critical load causing a column to buckle is of particular

Table 3.1 Boundary conditions for a two-dimensional beam

Type		$s = 0$	$s = 1$
1. Cantilever		$\theta = u = w = 0$	F_1, F_3, M_2
2. Both ends pinned		$M_2 = 0,$ $u = w = 0$	$F_1, M_2 = 0,$ $w = 0$
3. Slide against a fixed end		$\theta = u = w = 0$	$F_1,$ $\theta = w = 0$
4. Slide against an offset pinned end		M_2, u, w	$F_1,$ $\theta = w = 0$

concern, the models developed here relax several commonly made ideal-beam assumptions (such as constant constraints and small deflections) for practical robotic applications.

3.2 Three-Dimensional Beam

Figure 3.3 shows the 3D undeformed and deformed shapes of a flexible beam. The global reference frame is denoted as OXYZ; the local coordinate frames, "xyz" and "$\xi\eta\zeta$" (each with a subscript indicating its location along the beam path-length s), are defined in the undeformed and deformed configurations respectively. For examples, $x_0y_0z_0$ and $x_1y_1z_1$ are the local coordinate frames at P_0 and P_1 on both ends in the undeformed configuration, respectively. Similarly, $P_s(x_s,\ y_s,\ z_s)$ and $Q_s(\xi_s,\ \eta_s,\ \zeta_s)$ represent the same material point at the path-length s in the undeformed and deformed shapes respectively. All the coordinates follow the right-hand rule with x_s and ξ_s assigned along the neutral axis of the beam, and y_s, z_s, η_s and ζ_s are the principal axes on the corresponding cross-sections. In general, $P_0x_0y_0z_0$ differs from OXYZ with a translation and a rotation.

To facilitate the formulation, the unit vectors along the coordinate axes are denoted as follows:

$\mathbf{E}_1$, $\mathbf{E}_2$ and $\mathbf{E}_3$ are unit vectors along X, Y and Z axes, respectively.

$\mathbf{e}_1^{(0)}, \mathbf{e}_2^{(0)}$ and $\mathbf{e}_3^{(0)}$ are unit vectors along principal axes of x_s, y_s and z_s, respectively.

$\mathbf{e}_1$, $\mathbf{e}_2$ and $\mathbf{e}_3$ are unit vectors along principal axes of ξ_s, η_s and ζ_s, respectively.

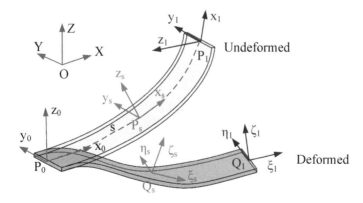

Fig. 3.3 Coordinates for a 3D compliant beam

The initial and deformed curves of the beam axis, $\left\{\mathbf{e}_i^{(0)}\right\}$ and $\{\mathbf{e}_i\}$ ($i = 1, 2, 3$), can be obtained by the following relations:

$$\mathbf{e}_i^{(0)} = R_{ij}^{(0)} \mathbf{E}_j \qquad\qquad (3.7a)$$

$$\mathbf{e}_i = R_{ij} \mathbf{E}_j \qquad\qquad (3.7b)$$

In (3.7), $R_{ij}^{(0)}$ and R_{ij} (i and j = 1, 2, 3), the components of the rotational matrixes $[\mathbf{R}]^{(0)}$ and $[\mathbf{R}]$ respectively, are functions of the path length s. It is noted that the bases $\left\{\mathbf{e}_i^{(0)}\right\}$ and $\{\mathbf{e}_i\}$ only characterize the axial curve of the beam. To account for the 3D beam geometry, one more variable $\varphi(s)$ is needed to quantify the twisting of the cross section relative to the beam axis.

Since the initial (or deformed) beam geometry is readily determined by $[\mathbf{R}]^{(0)}$ and $\varphi^{(0)}$ (or $[\mathbf{R}]$ and φ), the task is to find the rotational matrix and twisting angle. Because only three components among the rotational matrix elements and twisting angle are independent, it is better to reduce the order of the problem by using three independent components; namely, the curvature. So the formulation is based on vector superposition of curvatures as given in (3.8) implying that the deformed curvature $\mathbf{K} = [k_1 \ k_2 \ k_3]^{\mathrm{T}}$ is the summation of the initial curvature $\mathbf{K}^{(0)} = \left[k_1^{(0)} \ k_2^{(0)} \ k_3^{(0)}\right]^{\mathrm{T}}$ and the elastic curvature $\mathbf{K}^{(e)} = \left[k_1^{(e)} \ k_2^{(e)} \ k_3^{(e)}\right]^{\mathrm{T}}$ due to an external loading (of force $\mathbf{F}$ and moment $\mathbf{M}$):

$$\mathbf{K} = \mathbf{K}^{(0)} + \mathbf{K}^{(e)} \qquad\qquad (3.8)$$

In summary, thirteen variables are involved in formulating the beam deformation problem; namely, the nodal coordinates $\mathbf{x} = [x_s \ y_s \ z_s]^{\mathrm{T}}$, the orientations including first row of $\mathbf{R}_1 = [R_{11} \ R_{12} \ R_{13}]$ and the twisting angle φ, the force $\mathbf{F} = [F_1 \ F_2 \ F_3]^{\mathrm{T}}$ and moment $\mathbf{M} = [M_1 \ M_2 \ M_3]^{\mathrm{T}}$. The thirteen state variables are organized as $\mathbf{X} = [x_s \ y_s \ z_s; \ R_{11} \ R_{12} \ R_{13} \ \varphi; \ F_1 \ F_2 \ F_3 \ M_1 \ M_2 \ M_3]^{\mathrm{T}}$ with one constraint relation $R_{11}^2 + R_{12}^2 + R_{13}^2 = 1$.

Since the undeformed shape of the beam is known, $\mathbf{K}^{(0)}$ can be calculated. The components of the elastic curvature $\mathbf{K}^{(e)} = \left[k_1^{(e)} \ k_2^{(e)} \ k_3^{(e)}\right]^{\mathrm{T}}$ due to external loadings can be calculated as

$$k_i^{(e)} = \frac{\mathbf{M} \cdot \mathbf{e}_i}{(EI)} = \frac{M_k \mathbf{E}_k \cdot R_{ij} \mathbf{E}_j}{(EI)} = \frac{M_j R_{ij}}{(EI)} \qquad\qquad (3.9)$$

where $k_1^{(e)}$ is the twisting curvature, $k_2^{(e)}$ and $k_3^{(e)}$ are the bending curvatures, $(EI) = GI_1$ for $i = 1$, $(EI) = EI_i$ for $i = 2$ and 3, E is the Young's modulus, G is the shear modulus, and I_i ($i = 1, 2$ and 3) is the moment of inertia. Then, the longi-tudinal strain ε is given by (3.10) with A denoting the cross-section area

$$\varepsilon = \frac{\mathbf{F} \cdot \mathbf{e}_1}{EA} = \frac{F_i \mathbf{E}_i \cdot R_{1j} \mathbf{E}_j}{EA} = \frac{F_i R_{1i}}{EA} \qquad (3.10)$$

Based on the static analysis of the beam segment, the equations for the force and moment equilibrium are given by

$$-\mathbf{F} + (\mathbf{F} + \Delta\mathbf{F}) + \int_s^{s+\Delta s} \mathbf{q}_F d\rho = 0$$

$$-\mathbf{M} + (\mathbf{M} + \Delta\mathbf{M}) + \int_s^{s+\Delta s} \mathbf{q}_M d\rho + [\mathbf{e}_1(1+\varepsilon)\Delta s] \times (\mathbf{F} + \Delta\mathbf{F})$$

$$+ \int_s^{s+\Delta s} [\mathbf{e}_1(\rho - s)] \times \mathbf{q}_F d\rho = 0$$

where $\Delta\mathbf{R} = \text{skew}(\mathbf{K})\Delta s$. In the above moment equilibrium equations, all the moment terms are presented with respect to point Q_s in Fig. 3.4.

For an infinitesimally small Δs and neglecting the higher order terms, the above can be rewritten as

$$\frac{d\mathbf{F}}{ds} = -\mathbf{q}_F \qquad (3.11a)$$

$$\frac{d\mathbf{M}}{ds} = -\mathbf{q}_M - [(1+\varepsilon)\mathbf{e}_1] \times \mathbf{F} \qquad (3.11b)$$

Grouping (2.22) and (3.11), the governing equations of a 3D beam are

$$R'_{11} = k_3 R_{21} - k_2 R_{31} \qquad (3.12a)$$

$$R'_{12} = k_3 R_{22} - k_2 R_{32} \qquad (3.12b)$$

$$R'_{13} = k_3 R_{23} - k_2 R_{33} \qquad (3.12c)$$

Fig. 3.4 Equilibrium of a
beam segment

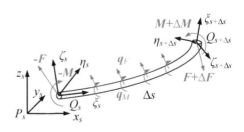

$$\varphi' = k_1 + k_2 \frac{R_{13}R_{32} - R_{12}R_{33}}{1 + R_{11}} + k_3 \frac{R_{12}R_{23} - R_{13}R_{22}}{1 + R_{11}} \tag{3.12d}$$

$$x'_s = (1+\varepsilon)R_{11} \tag{3.12e}$$

$$y'_s = (1+\varepsilon)R_{12} \tag{3.12f}$$

$$z'_s = (1+\varepsilon)R_{13} \tag{3.12g}$$

$$F'_1 = -q_{F1} \tag{3.12h}$$

$$F'_2 = -q_{F2} \tag{3.12i}$$

$$F'_3 = -q_{F3} \tag{3.12j}$$

$$M'_1 = -q_{M1} - (1+\varepsilon)(R_{12}F_3 - R_{13}F_2) \tag{3.12k}$$

$$M'_2 = -q_{M2} - (1+\varepsilon)(R_{13}F_1 - R_{11}F_3) \tag{3.12l}$$

$$M'_3 = -q_{M3} - (1+\varepsilon)(R_{11}F_2 - R_{12}F_1) \tag{3.12m}$$

where the prime denotes derivative with respect to s, and ε and $\mathbf{K} = [k_1 \ k_2 \ k_3]^{\mathrm{T}}$ are given by

$$\varepsilon = \frac{1}{EA}(F_1 R_{11} + F_2 R_{12} + F_3 R_{13}) \tag{3.13a}$$

$$k_1 = k_1^{(0)} + \frac{1}{GI_1}(M_1 R_{11} + M_2 R_{12} + M_3 R_{13}) \tag{3.13b}$$

$$k_2 = k_2^{(0)} + \frac{1}{EI_2}(M_1 R_{21} + M_2 R_{22} + M_3 R_{23}) \tag{3.13c}$$

$$k_3 = k_3^{(0)} + \frac{1}{GI_3}(M_1 R_{31} + M_2 R_{32} + M_3 R_{33}) \tag{3.13d}$$

For design purposes, the following normalized variables are applied to the beam equations (3.12):

$$\frac{M_i}{\tilde{M}_i} = \frac{F_i L}{\tilde{F}_i} = \frac{q_{Mi}L}{\tilde{q}_{Mi}} = \frac{q_{Fi}L^2}{\tilde{q}_{Fi}} = \frac{EI_2}{L}$$

$$\frac{k_i^{(0)}}{\tilde{k}_i^{(0)}} = \frac{k_i}{\tilde{k}_i} = \frac{1}{L}, \frac{x_s}{\tilde{x}_s} = \frac{y_s}{\tilde{y}_s} = \frac{z_s}{\tilde{z}_s} = L$$

where L is the beam length. Then (3.12) is recast and the differentiation is carried out with respect to the normalized path length, $\tilde{s} = s/L$.

$$\mathbf{R}'_1 = \tilde{k}_3 \mathbf{R}_2 - \tilde{k}_2 \mathbf{R}_3 \tag{3.14a}$$

$$\varphi' = \tilde{k}_1 + \tilde{k}_2 \frac{R_{13}R_{32} - R_{12}R_{33}}{1 + R_{11}} + \tilde{k}_3 \frac{R_{12}R_{23} - R_{13}R_{22}}{1 + R_{11}} \tag{3.14b}$$

$$\tilde{\mathbf{x}}' = (1 + \varepsilon)\mathbf{R}_1 \tag{3.14c}$$

$$\tilde{\mathbf{F}}' = -\tilde{\mathbf{q}}_F \tag{3.14d}$$

$$\tilde{\mathbf{M}}' = -\tilde{\mathbf{q}}_M - [(1 + \varepsilon)\mathbf{e}_1] \times \tilde{\mathbf{F}} \tag{3.14e}$$

where the prime denotes derivative with respect to s; $\mathbf{R}_i$ (i = 1, 2 and 3) is the ith row of the rotational matrix $[\mathbf{R}]$ between the frames $P_0 x_0 y_0 z_0$ and $P_s x_s y_s z_s$; φ is the twisting angle; $\tilde{\mathbf{x}} = [\tilde{x}_s \, \tilde{y}_s \, \tilde{z}_s]^{\mathrm{T}}$ is the normalized nodal coordinate; $\tilde{\mathbf{F}} = [\tilde{F}_1 \, \tilde{F}_2 \, \tilde{F}_3]^{\mathrm{T}}$ and $\tilde{\mathbf{M}} = [\tilde{M}_1 \, \tilde{M}_2 \, \tilde{M}_3]^{\mathrm{T}}$ are the normalized nodal force and moment; $\tilde{\mathbf{q}}_F = [\tilde{q}_{F1} \, \tilde{q}_{F2} \, \tilde{q}_{F3}]^{\mathrm{T}}$ and $\tilde{\mathbf{q}}_M = [\tilde{q}_{M1} \, \tilde{q}_{M2} \, \tilde{q}_{M3}]^{\mathrm{T}}$ are the normalized distributed force and moment, respectively. The longitudinal strain ε and curvatures $\mathbf{K}^{(e)}$ are calculated as follows

$$\tilde{\varepsilon} = \frac{I_2}{AL^2}\tilde{\mathbf{F}} \cdot \mathbf{R}_1 \tag{3.15a}$$

$$\tilde{\kappa}_1 = \tilde{k}_1^{(0)} + \frac{EI_2}{GI_1}\tilde{\mathbf{M}} \cdot \mathbf{R}_1 \tag{3.15b}$$

$$\tilde{\kappa}_2 = \tilde{k}_2^{(0)} + \tilde{\mathbf{M}} \cdot \mathbf{R}_2 \tag{3.15c}$$

$$\tilde{\kappa}_3 = \tilde{k}_3^{(0)} + \frac{I_2}{I_3}\tilde{\mathbf{M}} \cdot \mathbf{R}_3 \tag{3.15d}$$

The boundary conditions for a 3D flexible beam are given by thirteen algebraic equations for the state variable vector $\mathbf{X}$ at both beam ends $s = 0$ and $s = L$. Table 3.2 summarizes four typical boundary conditions, which are also commonly specified for analyzing columns. For a cantilever (Type 1) where the slope and displacements are zeros at the fixed end, the forces and moments at the free end must be specified. For a beam with both ends constrained with pin-joints (Type 2), the displacement constraints cannot sustain any moment; $\mathbf{M} = 0$ but $\mathbf{F}$ must be specified. As will be illustrated, Types 3 and 4 are specified for sensor attachment and for negotiating a convex corner, respectively. Type 3 is similar to Type 2 but can resist nonzero moments while maintaining zero slopes at both ends. In Type 4, a nonzero moment can be exerted against an offset pinned end. Two examples are provided to illustrate the boundary conditions.

Table 3.2 Boundary conditions for a three-dimensional beam

Type	$s = 0$	$s = 1$
 1. Cantilever	$R_{11} = 1,\ R_{12} = 0,\ R_{13} = 0,\ \varphi = 0,\ x_s = x_s^{(0)},\ y_s = y_s^{(0)},\ z_s = z_s^{(0)}$	$F_1, F_2, F_3,$ M_1, M_2, M_3
 2. Both ends pinned	$x_s = x_s^{(0)},\ y_s = y_s^{(0)},\ z_s = z_s^{(0)}$ $M_1 = M_2 = M_3 = 0$	$z_s = z_s^{(0)};$ $F_1, F_2, F_3;$ $M_1 = M_2 = M_3 = 0$
 3. Slide against a fixed end	$R_{11} = 1,\ R_{12} = R_{13} = \varphi = 0;$ $x_s = x_s^{(0)},\ y_s = y_s^{(0)},\ z_s = z_s^{(0)}$	$R_{11} = 1,\ R_{12} = R_{13} = 0;\ y_s = y_s^{(0)},\ z_s = z_s^{(0)};$ F_1
 4. Slide against an offset pinned end	$R_{11} = 1,\ R_{12} = R_{13} = \varphi = 0;$ $y_s = y_s^{(0)},\ z_s = z_s^{(0)};$ F_1	$x_s, y_s, z_s;$ M_1, M_2, M_3

Example 3.2.1 A Compressive Spring

In this example, the compressive spring is modeled as a helix curved beam with a circular cross-section. Its initial curvature has been studied in Example 2.3.2 but the case is now considered under axial compression. Table 3.3 lists the spring specifications in terms of the dimensions and material properties. The boundary conditions show that one end of the spring is rigidly fixed while the other end is free and subjected to axial compression. As shown in Fig. 3.5, instability can occur for spring under axial compression, and the model produces a close result (percentage error = 3.96%) with finite element analysis.

Example 3.2.2 A Twisted Ring

A compliant half-ring mechanism is pinned at both ends and twisted by an angle θ, and the parametric values for four different materials (steel, titanium, aluminum and delrin) are shown in Table 3.4. For design purposes, the results are presented in non-dimensional forms; the following normalization rules are applied to (3.12):

Table 3.3 Spring specification and boundary conditions

Dimension		Material properties	
Radius (mm)	7.239	Elastic modulus (GPa)	193
Pitch (mm)	5.715	Shear modulus (GPa)	80.8
Cross section radius (mm)	0.6985	Poisson ratio	0.25
Boundary conditions			
$s = 0$	$x_s = 0,\ y_s = 0,\ z_s = 0,\ R_{11} = 1,\ R_{12} = 0,\ R_{13} = 0,$ $\varphi = 0;$		
$s = L$	$F_1 = 0,\ F_2 = 0,\ F_3 = F,\ M_1 = 0,\ M_2 = 0,\ M_3 = 0.$		

Fig. 3.5 Lateral deflection under axial compression

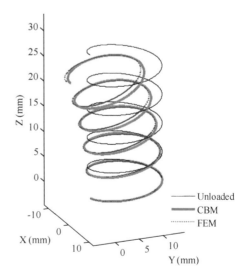

Table 3.4 Ring specification and boundary conditions

Parameters	Steel	Titanium	Aluminum	Delrin
E (GPa)	193	116	70	3.1
Poisson ratio	0.25	0.34	0.3	0.35
Density(10^3 kg/m^3)	7.85	4.54	2.7	1.42

$b/h = 2;\ \theta = \pi/4$

$s/r = 0,$
$R_{11} = \cos\theta,\ R_{12} = \sin\theta,\ R_{13} = 0$
$x_0 = y_0 = z_0 = \varphi = 0$

$s/r = \pi,$
$R_{12} = \sin\theta,\ R_{13} = 0,$
$x_1 = 0,\ z_1 = 0,\ \varphi = 0$

$$\frac{M_i}{\tilde{M}_i} = \frac{F_i r}{\tilde{F}_i} = \frac{q_{Mi} r}{\tilde{q}_{Mi}} = \frac{q_{Fi} r^2}{\tilde{q}_{Fi}} = \frac{EI_2}{r}$$

$$\frac{k_i^{(0)}}{\tilde{k}_i^{(0)}} = \frac{k_i}{\tilde{k}_i} = \frac{1}{r},\ \frac{x_s}{\tilde{x}_s} = \frac{y_s}{\tilde{y}_s} = \frac{z_s}{\tilde{z}_s} = r$$

where r is radius of the ring.

The deformed shape of the compliant ring ($b/h = 2$) is simulated in Fig. 3.6 when the ring is subjected to a pure twisting of $\theta = \pi/4$ at both ends. The effects of aspect ratios ($b/h = 2, 3, 6$) and material properties on the (normalized) twisting moment M_2 along Y axis at both ends are compared in Fig. 3.7. It is shown that the normalized twisting moment M_2 is more sensitive to the aspect ratios (b/h) than the material properties.

3.3 Annular Plate

Figure 3.8 schematically shows an annular thin-wall plate (outer radius a, inner radius b, and thickness h), where [$\mathbf{e}_r\ \mathbf{e}_\theta\ \mathbf{e}_z$] is the cylindrical reference frame located at the plate center with $\mathbf{e}_z$ normal to the curvilinear axes ($\mathbf{e}_r$ and $\mathbf{e}_\theta$) on the referenced mid-surface. In Fig. 3.8, φ_1 and φ_2 are two rotation angles of a plate element with respect to $\mathbf{e}_r$ and $\mathbf{e}_\theta$ due to shear deformations, and they are given by

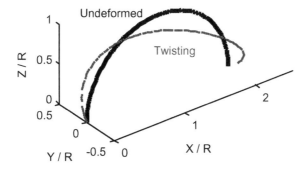

Fig. 3.6 Normalized deformed shape of the twisted ring

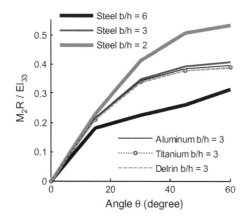

Fig. 3.7 Effect of aspect ratios and materials

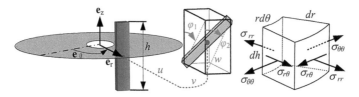

Fig. 3.8 An element in a thin-wall plate

$$\sin \varphi_1 \simeq \varphi_1 \simeq -\frac{\partial w}{r \partial \theta} \text{ and } \sin \varphi_2 \simeq \varphi_2 \simeq \frac{\partial w}{\partial r}.$$

A plate element of thickness h is shown to displace by $u\mathbf{e}_r + v\mathbf{e}_\theta + w\mathbf{e}_z$, and orient by φ_1 around $\mathbf{e}_r$ and φ_2 around $\mathbf{e}_\theta$. Then the displacement of any point on the element $(-h/2 \leq z \leq h/2)$ is

$$\mathbf{D} = (u + z \sin \varphi_2)\mathbf{e}_r + (v - z \sin \varphi_1)\mathbf{e}_\theta + w\mathbf{e}_z \tag{3.16}$$

For small deformations, the in-plane displacements u and v are negligible when compared to the out-of-plane displacement w. Along with the stress-strain relation (3.17) for isotropic materials, the force and moment vectors $(\mathbf{q}, \boldsymbol{\eta})$ acting on the element are expressed as a function of $w(t, r, \theta)$ in (3.18):

$$\boldsymbol{\sigma} = \begin{bmatrix} \sigma_{rr} \\ \sigma_{\theta\theta} \\ \sigma_{r\theta} \end{bmatrix} = \frac{E}{1-v^2} \begin{bmatrix} 1 & v & 0 \\ v & 1 & 0 \\ 0 & 0 & (1-v)/2 \end{bmatrix} \begin{bmatrix} \varepsilon_{rr} \\ \varepsilon_{\theta\theta} \\ 2\varepsilon_{r\theta} \end{bmatrix} \tag{3.17a}$$

where

$$\boldsymbol{\varepsilon} = \begin{bmatrix} \varepsilon_{rr} \\ \varepsilon_{\theta\theta} \\ \varepsilon_{r\theta} \end{bmatrix} = \frac{1}{2} \begin{bmatrix} w_r^2 - 2zw_{rr} \\ (w_\theta/r)^2 - 2z(w_{\theta\theta} + rw_r)/r^2 \\ w_\theta w_r/r + 2z(w_\theta - rw_{r\theta})/r^2 \end{bmatrix} \tag{3.17b}$$

The internal force $\mathbf{q}$ and moment $\boldsymbol{\eta}$ are

$$\begin{bmatrix} \mathbf{q} \\ \boldsymbol{\eta} \end{bmatrix} = \int_{-h/2}^{h/2} \begin{bmatrix} \boldsymbol{\sigma} \\ \boldsymbol{\sigma}z \end{bmatrix} dz \tag{3.18}$$

where $\mathbf{q} = [q_{rr} \quad q_{\theta\theta} \quad q_{r\theta}]^T$ and $\boldsymbol{\eta} = [\eta_{rr} \quad \eta_{\theta\theta} \quad \eta_{r\theta}]^T$. Using the Hamilton principle and taking the variations, the equation for the element subjected to a centrifugal force f is derived as

$$m\ddot{w} + c\dot{w} + kw = f(t, r, \theta; \Omega) \tag{3.19}$$

where the operators ($\mathbf{m}$, $\mathbf{c}$ and $\mathbf{k}$ characterizing the elemental inertias, damping and elasticity) are explicitly written as

$$\mathbf{m} = \rho h - I_2 \nabla^2, \ \mathbf{c} = \mu, \ \mathbf{k} = \frac{Eh^3}{12(1-v^2)} \nabla^2 \nabla^2 \tag{3.20a–c}$$

where ρ, μ E and v are the density, damping coefficient, elastic modulus and Poisson ratio of the material, $I_2 = (\rho h^3/12)$ is the moment of inertia about the neutral axis, and the Laplace operator in polar coordinates is

$$\nabla^2 = \frac{\partial^2}{\partial r^2} + \frac{\partial}{r\partial r} + \frac{\partial^2}{r^2\partial\theta^2}$$

For a thin-wall plate rotating at a constant speed Ω, the centrifugal force acting on the plate can be obtained as [1]:

$$
\begin{aligned}
f = &-\frac{\rho h}{2}(r\Omega)^2\left(\nabla^2 w + 2\frac{\partial w}{r\partial r}\right) + q_{rr}\frac{\partial^2 w}{\partial r^2} \\
&+ q_{\theta\theta}\left(\frac{\partial w}{r\partial r} + \frac{\partial^2 w}{r^2\partial\theta^2}\right) + q_{r\theta}\left(\frac{2\partial^2 w}{r\partial r\partial\theta} - \frac{2\partial w}{r^2\partial\theta}\right)
\end{aligned}
\tag{3.21}
$$

where $\mathbf{q}$ is expressed in terms of the stress function $\psi(r,\theta)$ that depends on external loadings:

$$\mathbf{q}(\psi) = \left[\frac{\partial\psi}{r\partial r} + \frac{\partial^2\psi}{r^2\partial\theta^2} \quad \frac{\partial^2\psi}{\partial r^2} \quad \frac{\partial\psi}{r^2\partial\theta} - \frac{\partial^2\psi}{r\partial r\partial\theta}\right]^{\mathrm{T}} \tag{3.22}$$

For a system subjected to no external loading except the centrifugal force of a rotating plate, the stress function ψ in $\mathbf{q}$ of (3.21) is independent of θ and has the form:

$$\psi = \rho h\Omega^2 g(r) \tag{3.23}$$

As indicated in (3.22) that $\mathbf{q}$ only depends on derivatives of $g(r)$, it is not necessary to obtain $g(r)$ but its first derivative with respect to r, which was derived in [1] and is rewritten as

$$g'(r) = \frac{1}{8}\left[(1-v)r^3 + a^2 b_+ r + \frac{a^2 b^2 b_-}{r}\right]$$

where

$$b_\pm = \frac{(1\pm v)\left[3 + v \pm (1\mp v)\gamma_b^{3\pm 1}\right]}{1 + v + \gamma_b^2(1-v)}.$$

The displacement w is decoupled into a product of time and spatial distributions by the separation-of-variable method:

$$w(t,r,\theta) = \sum_{n=0}^{+\infty}\sum_{m=0}^{+\infty}[\phi_{nm}(r)e^{in\theta}]e^{i\omega_{nm}t} \tag{3.24}$$

where n is the nodal diameter, m is the nodal circle, ω_{nm} is the natural frequency; and ϕ_{nm} is the corresponding mode shape.

Formulation with Normalization

To capture the effects of process parameters (such as Ω and h) on the rotating plate dynamics for design analysis, the following normalization is carried out for modal analysis:

$$\frac{R}{r/a} = \frac{W}{w/h} = \frac{\Phi}{\phi/h} = 1, \frac{\tau}{t} = \frac{hc_w}{a^2}, \frac{\overline{\Omega}}{\Omega} = \frac{\overline{\omega}}{\omega} = \frac{a^2}{hc_w} \tag{3.25a–f}$$

$$\text{where} \quad c_w = \sqrt{\frac{E}{12\rho(1-v^2)}}; \gamma_h = \frac{h}{a} \text{ and } \gamma_b = \frac{b}{a}.$$

In this way, the dynamic model (3.19) has the normalized form,

$$\mathbf{M}\ddot{W} + \mathbf{C}\dot{W} + \mathbf{K}W = F(\tau, R, \theta; \overline{\Omega}) \tag{3.26a}$$

where $\mathbf{M} = 1 - \frac{\gamma_h^2}{12}\overline{\nabla}^2, \mathbf{C} = \bar{\mu}, \mathbf{K} = \overline{\nabla}^2\overline{\nabla}^2, \frac{\bar{\mu}}{\mu} = \frac{h\bar{q}}{q} = \frac{1}{\rho c_w \gamma_h^2}$ and

$$
\begin{aligned}
F = {} & -\frac{R^2\overline{\Omega}^2}{2}\left(\overline{\nabla}^2 W + 2\frac{\partial W}{R\partial R}\right) + \bar{q}_{rr}\frac{\partial^2 W}{\partial R^2} \\
& + \bar{q}_{\theta\theta}\left(\frac{\partial W}{R\partial R} + \frac{\partial^2 W}{R^2\partial\theta^2}\right) + \bar{q}_{r\theta}\left(\frac{2\partial^2 W}{R\partial R\partial\theta} - \frac{2\partial W}{R^2\partial\theta}\right)
\end{aligned}
\tag{3.26b–g}
$$

With the normalization rules presented in (3.25), the displacement w in (3.24) can be written as

$$W(\tau, R, \theta) = \sum_{n=0}^{+\infty}\sum_{m=0}^{+\infty}[\Phi_{nm}(R)e^{in\theta}]e^{i\overline{\omega}_{nm}\tau} \tag{3.27}$$

Considering the variable separated form of W given in (3.27)

$$\overline{\nabla}^2 W = \nabla_R^2 W \tag{3.28}$$

where $\nabla_R^2 = \frac{\partial^2}{\partial R^2} + \frac{\partial}{R\partial R} - \frac{n^2}{R^2}$, indicating that the Laplace operator on (3.27) is equivalent to an operator ∇_R^2 that only affects the $\Phi_{nm}(R)$ component.

The normalized forms of (3.23) and (3.22) are

$$\Psi = \overline{\Omega}^2 \bar{g}(R) \tag{3.29}$$

$$\bar{q}(R) = \overline{\Omega}^2[\bar{g}'(R)/R \quad \bar{g}''(R) \quad 0]^T \tag{3.30}$$

where

$$\frac{\Psi}{\psi} = \frac{1}{\rho h^3 c_w^2}, \ \bar{g}'(R) = \frac{1}{8}\left[(1-v)R^3 + b_+ R + \frac{\gamma_b^2 b_-}{R}\right].$$

Substituting (3.24) into (3.19) for an undamped ($\mu = 0$) rotating plate system is equivalent to substituting (3.27) into (3.26a) with $\bar{\mu} = 0$, where the left hand side of (3.26a) can be obtained as

$$\sum_{n=0}^{+\infty}\sum_{m=0}^{+\infty}\left[-\left(1 - \frac{\gamma_h^2}{12}\right)\bar{\omega}_{nm}^2 \Phi_{nm}(R) + \nabla_R^2 \nabla_R^2 \Phi_{nm}(R)\right]e^{in\theta}e^{i\bar{\omega}_{nm}\tau}$$

and the right-hand side becomes

$$\sum_{n=0}^{+\infty}\sum_{m=0}^{+\infty}\left[-\frac{R^2\bar{\Omega}^2}{2}\left(\nabla_R^2 + 2\frac{d}{RdR}\right)\Phi_{nm}\right]e^{in\theta}e^{i\bar{\omega}_{nm}\tau}$$

$$+\bar{\Omega}^2\frac{\bar{g}'}{R}\sum_{n=0}^{+\infty}\sum_{m=0}^{+\infty}\frac{d^2\Phi_{nm}}{dR^2}e^{in\theta}e^{i\bar{\omega}_{nm}\tau} + \bar{\Omega}^2\bar{g}''\sum_{n=0}^{+\infty}\sum_{m=0}^{+\infty}\left[\left(\frac{d}{RdR} - \frac{n^2}{R^2}\right)\Phi_{nm}\right]e^{in\theta}e^{i\bar{\omega}_{nm}\tau}$$

So (3.26a) is modified as

$$\nabla_R^2 \nabla_R^2 \Phi_{nm}(R) + \bar{\Omega}^2 \Gamma[\Phi_{nm}(R)] - \left(1 - \frac{\gamma_h^2}{12}\right)\bar{\omega}_{nm}^2 \Phi_{nm}(R) = 0 \qquad (3.31)$$

where $\quad \Gamma[\Phi_{nm}(R)] = \left[\frac{R^2}{2}\left(\nabla_R^2 + \frac{2d}{RdR}\right) - \bar{g}'\frac{d^2}{RdR^2} - \bar{g}''\left(\frac{d}{RdR} - \frac{n^2}{R^2}\right)\right]\Phi_{nm}(R).$

It is noted that (3.31) is a fourth order differential equation of $\Phi_{nm}(R)$, which can be expanded into (3.32):

$$\frac{\partial^4 \Phi_{nm}}{\partial R^4} + \frac{2}{R}\frac{\partial^3 \Phi_{nm}}{\partial R^3} + \frac{b_2}{R^2}\frac{\partial^2 \Phi_{nm}}{\partial R^2} + \frac{b_1}{R^3}\frac{\partial \Phi_{nm}}{\partial R} + \frac{b_0}{R^4}\Phi_{nm} = 0 \qquad (3.32)$$

where

$$b_0 = n^2(n^2 - 4) - \frac{n^2\bar{\Omega}^2}{8}\left[(1-3v)R^4 + b_+ R^2 - \gamma_b^2 b_-\right] - \left(R^2 - \frac{n^2\gamma_h^2}{12}\right)\bar{\omega}_{nm}^2 R^2,$$

$$b_1 = (1+2n^2) + \frac{\bar{\Omega}^2}{8}\left[3(3-v)R^4 - b_+ R^2 + \gamma_b^2 b_-\right] + \frac{\gamma_h^2}{12}\bar{\omega}_{nm}^2 R^2,$$

$$b_2 = -(1+2n^2) + \frac{\bar{\Omega}^2}{8}\left[(3-v)R^4 + b_+ R^2 + \gamma_b^2 b_-\right] + \frac{\gamma_h^2}{12}\bar{\omega}_{nm}^2 R^2.$$

The above formulation captures the thin-wall plate vibration in both time and spatial domains, and characterizes the distributed inertia, stiffness and damping effects in terms of intuitive "mass-spring-damper" mathematic operators.

The vibration displacement field of an annular plate can be uniquely determined for a specified set of boundary conditions (BCs) imposed by the (displacement or loading) constraints of the forms

$$w = 0, \ \frac{\partial w}{\partial r} = 0 \tag{3.33a, b}$$

$$\eta_{rr} = 0, \ rq_{rz} + \frac{\partial \eta_{r\theta}}{\partial \theta} = 0 \tag{3.33c, d}$$

where η_{rr} and $\eta_{r\theta}$ are the bending and shear moments, respectively; and q_{rz} is the shear force defined in (3.18). Four types of BCs can be provided to adapt an annular plate for different application purposes.

BC1: Fixed edge, (3.33a,b)
BC2: Pinned edge, (3.33a,c)
BC3: Sliding edge, (3.33b,d)
BC4: Free edge, (3.33c,d)

From (3.33a,b) and (3.27) that

$$\phi_{nm} = 0, \ \phi'_{nm} = 0 \tag{3.34a, b}$$

From (3.17a) and (3.18), the moments are obtained in terms of displacement as

$$\begin{bmatrix} \eta_{rr} \\ \eta_{\theta\theta} \\ \eta_{r\theta} \end{bmatrix} = -\frac{Eh^3}{12(1 - \upsilon^2)} \begin{bmatrix} 1 & \upsilon & 0 \\ \upsilon & 1 & 0 \\ 0 & 0 & 1-\upsilon \end{bmatrix} \begin{bmatrix} \frac{\partial^2 w}{\partial r^2} \\ \frac{\partial^2 w}{r^2 \partial \theta^2} + \frac{\partial w}{r \partial r} \\ \frac{\partial^2 w}{r \partial r \partial \theta} - \frac{\partial w}{r^2 \partial \theta} \end{bmatrix}$$

Substituting (3.24) into (3.33c,d) arrives at

$$\sum_{n=0}^{+\infty} \sum_{m=0}^{+\infty} [\phi''_{nm}(r) e^{in\theta}] e^{i\omega_{nm}t} + \upsilon(-\frac{n^2}{r^2} + \frac{d}{rdr}) \sum_{n=0}^{+\infty} \sum_{m=0}^{+\infty} [\phi_{nm}(r) e^{in\theta}] e^{i\omega_{nm}t} = 0$$

$$\text{or} \quad \phi''_{nm} + \upsilon(\frac{1}{r}\phi'_{nm} - \frac{n^2}{r^2}\phi_{nm}) = 0$$

$$\tag{3.34c}$$

Similarly, substituting (3.24) into (3.33d) arrives at

$$\phi'''_{nm} + \frac{1}{r}\phi''_{nm} - \frac{1 + 2n^2 - n^2\upsilon}{r^2}\phi'_{nm} + \frac{n^2(3 - \upsilon)}{r^3}\phi_{nm} = 0 \tag{3.34d}$$

As the moments are expressed in terms of displacement, the BCs (3.33a,b), (3.33c) and (3.33d) become (3.35a,b), (3.35c) and (3.35d) respectively:

$$\Phi_{nm} = \Phi'_{nm} = 0 \qquad (3.35a, b)$$

$$\Phi'''_{nm} + \Phi''_{nm} - (1 + 2n^2 - n^2 v)\Phi''_{nm} + n^2(3 - v)\Phi_{nm} = 0 \qquad (3.35c)$$

$$\Phi''_{nm} + v(\Phi'_{nm} - n^2\Phi_{nm}) = 0 \qquad (3.35d)$$

The prime in (3.35) denotes derivative with respect to the radius r. It is noted that (3.35a,b) are the normalized form of (3.34a,b) evaluated at $R = \gamma_b$, and (3.35c,d) are the normalized form of (3.34c,d) evaluated at $R = 1$.

With the BCs (3.35a–d) in mind, assuming

$$\Phi_{nm} = c_1\Phi^{(1)}_{nm} + c_2\Phi^{(2)}_{nm} \qquad (3.36)$$

where c_1 and c_2 are constants to be calculated, $\Phi^{(1)}_{nm}$ and $\Phi^{(2)}_{nm}$ satisfy (3.32) with the following initial conditions at $R = \gamma_b$.

$$\Phi^{(1)}_{nm} = \Phi^{(1)'}_{nm} = 0, \ \Phi^{(1)''}_{nm} = 1, \ \Phi^{(1)'''}_{nm} = 0 \qquad (3.37a–d)$$

$$\Phi^{(2)}_{nm} = \Phi^{(2)'}_{nm} = \Phi^{(2)''}_{nm} = 0, \ \Phi^{(2)'''}_{nm} = 1 \qquad (3.37e–h)$$

Equation (3.36) automatically satisfy (3.33a,b) at $R = \gamma_b$. For $R = 1$, substituting (3.36) into (3.35a,b) for a fixed constraint or (3.35c,d) for a free condition, a set of homogeneous equations can be obtained for the coefficients:

$$\mathbf{A}(\bar{\omega}_{nm})[c_1 \quad c_2]^{\mathrm{T}} = \mathbf{0} \qquad (3.38)$$

When the outer edge is fixed, $\mathbf{A}(\bar{\omega}_{nm}) = \begin{bmatrix} \Phi^{(1)}_{nm} & \Phi^{(2)}_{nm} \\ \Phi^{(1)'}_{nm} & \Phi^{(2)'}_{nm} \end{bmatrix}_{R=1}$,

and if the outer edge is free, $\mathbf{A}(\bar{\omega}_{nm}) = \begin{bmatrix} c^{(1)}_1 & c^{(2)}_1 \\ c^{(1)}_2 & c^{(2)}_2 \end{bmatrix}_{R=1}$,

where $c^{(i)}_1 = \Phi^{(i)'''}_{nm} + \Phi^{(i)''}_{nm} - (1 + 2n^2 - n^2 v)\Phi^{(i)'}_{nm} + n^2(3 - v)\Phi^{(i)}_{nm}$,

$c^{(i)}_2 = \Phi^{(i)''}_{nm} + v(\Phi^{(i)'}_{nm} - n^2\Phi^{(i)}_{nm})$, $i = 1$ and 2.

For a nontrivial solution of c_1 and c_2, the natural frequency ω_{nm} can be numerically solved from

$$|\mathbf{A}(\bar{\omega}_{nm})| = 0 \qquad (3.39)$$

The computation steps are organized as follows:

Step 1   For a specific value of n, obtain $\Phi_{nm}^{(1)}$ and $\Phi_{nm}^{(2)}$ by solving an initial value problem given by (3.32) and (3.37).

Step 2   Establish the homogeneous equation (3.38) and obtain a set of $\bar{\omega}_{nm}$ corresponding to the specific n in Step 1 by solving (3.39) numerically; for example, the multiple roots can be located by using a simple bisection method [2] with good convergence.

Step 3   For each $\bar{\omega}_{nm}$, the non-zero values of c_1 and c_2 are obtained from (3.38);

Step 4   The mode shape function Φ_{nm} corresponding to ω_{nm} is given by (3.36), and then divided by its norm for normalization to satisfy the following condition:

$$\int_{\gamma_h}^{1} |\Phi_{nm}(R)|^2 dR = 1$$

The mode shape function Φ_{nm} can also be numerically solved from the boundary problem given by (3.32) and (3.35) using a shooting method [2].

3.4   General Constraint

Figure 3.9 schematically illustrates a multi-body compliant mechanism consisting of N_r rigid bodies and N_c compliant elements, where $i = 1, 2, \ldots, N_r$ and $j = 1, 2, \ldots, N_c$. The rigid bodies, each of which has multi-DOFs with respect to the global (reference) coordinate system XYZ, are constrained by (rotational and/or sliding) joints or contact (between two rigid bodies i and $i + 1$) while the compliant elements (capable of deforming in the 3D space) may be fixed or pinned on the rigid bodies. External forces and moments (denoted as $\mathbf{f}_i$ and τ_i and $\mathbf{F}_j$ and $\mathbf{M}_j$ in Fig. 3.9 respectively) are applied to the ith rigid body and/or the jth compliant elements. The problem can be formulated in two opposing ways, which are referred to here as forward and inverse problems. The former solves for deformation of the system

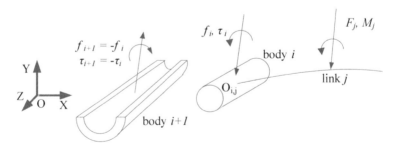

Fig. 3.9 Multi-body compliant mechanism

Fig. 3.10 Bio-joint
constraint

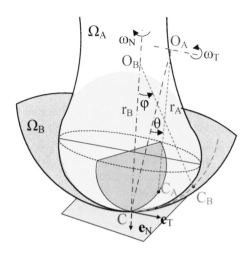

given the external loadings while the latter determines the required forces/moments
for a specified deformed configuration.

The general constraint is formulated for motions between two rigid bodies, Ω_A and
Ω_B, which are bounded by boundaries Γ_A and Γ_B respectively. As shown in Fig. 3.10,
Ω_A rolls on Ω_B, and C is an instantaneous contact point satisfying (3.40a,b),

$$\mathbf{P}_A(\mathbf{x}_c) = \mathbf{P}_B(\mathbf{x}_c) \text{ and } \mathbf{P}'_A(\mathbf{x}_c) = \mathbf{P}'_B(\mathbf{x}_c) \qquad (3.40a, b)$$

where $\mathbf{P}_A(\mathbf{x})$ and $\mathbf{P}_B(\mathbf{x})$ describe the contact points on Ω_A and Ω_B in terms of a
position vector $\mathbf{x}$ in the world frame; $\mathbf{P}'_A(\mathbf{x})$ and $\mathbf{P}'_B(\mathbf{x})$ are their derivatives with
respect to $\mathbf{x}$; and the subscript "c" denotes the contact point C. It is worth noting
that common engineering joints and mechanical cams are special cases of the
general constraint referred as the biological joint as illustrated in Fig. 3.10.

Given C on Γ_A, there always exists a tangential plane with a normal vector $\mathbf{e}_N$
such that the angular velocity $\boldsymbol{\omega}$ describes the motion of Ω_A at C,

$$\boldsymbol{\omega} = \omega_N \mathbf{e}_N + \omega_T \mathbf{e}_T \qquad (3.41)$$

where $\mathbf{e}_T$ is a unit vector on the tangential plane. An osculating plane is defined
(indicated in blue in Fig. 3.10) perpendicular to ω_T at C. The contact point on Γ_A
and Γ_B moves incrementally from C_A and C_B to C along the respective osculating
circles as shown in Fig. 3.10, where (O_A, ρ_A) and (O_B, ρ_B) are the centers and radii
of the osculating circles intersecting at Γ_A and Γ_B respectively; and θ and φ are the
angles describing the corresponding displacements of the contact points on Ω_A and
Ω_B respectively. The 3D motions of a biological joint can be characterized in the
instantaneous osculating plane that depends on the location of the contact point
(and hence is a function of time).

The contact point displacement of Ω_A is

$$ds = \sqrt{(ds_N)^2 + (ds_T)^2} = ds_T \sqrt{1 + (\omega_N dt)^2} \approx ds_T \qquad (3.42)$$

where $ds_T = \rho_A \omega_T dt$ and $ds_N = ds_T \omega_N dt$ are in the $\mathbf{e}_T$ and $\mathbf{e}_N$ directions, when neglecting the higher order infinitesimal time interval dt^2. Without loss of generality, the effect of ω_N (that may be nonzero) on the contact point displacement s is neglected; $\omega_T = \omega$ is assumed to simplify analysis of the biological kinematics in the following discussion. The 3D kinematics of a biological joint is reduced to finding the contact location in the osculating motion and the position and orientation of Ω_A. In addition, the boundaries (Γ_A and Γ_B) are assumed to be known with respect to their own local coordinate frames. In a polar coordinate, a smooth 2D curve on the boundary is denoted as

$$\mathbf{P}[\mathbf{x}(\psi)] = \mathbf{P}[x(\psi), y(\psi)] = x(\psi)\mathbf{E}_1 + y(\psi)\mathbf{E}_2 \qquad (3.43)$$

where ψ is an angle with respect to the reference body axis. The tangential and normal directions at $\mathbf{x}$ on the curve are

$$\mathbf{e}_T = \mathbf{P}' = \frac{dx}{d\psi}\mathbf{E}_1 + \frac{dy}{d\psi}\mathbf{E}_2, \text{ and } \mathbf{e}_N = -\frac{dy}{d\psi}\mathbf{E}_1 + \frac{dx}{d\psi}\mathbf{E}_2 \qquad (3.44\text{a, b})$$

The radius of an osculating circle can be obtained according to [3]:

$$r = \frac{|\mathbf{P}'|^3}{|\mathbf{P}' \times \mathbf{P}''|} \qquad (3.45)$$

For a sliding contact, there is a relative velocity v_r between Ω_A and Ω_B,

$$r_A \omega_\tau = r_B (d\varphi/dt) + v_r \text{ where } \omega_T = d\theta/dt. \qquad (3.46)$$

The lengths of CC_A and CC_B, in the polar coordinate, are respectively given by (3.47a) and (3.47b), where "$\sim$" refers to the value of the dummy variable in the curve equation:

$$s + \int_0^{t_c} v_r dt = \int_0^{t_c} r_A \omega_T dt = \int_{\tilde{\theta}_0}^{\tilde{\theta}_c} |\mathbf{P}'_A[x(\psi), y(\psi)]| d\psi \qquad (3.47\text{a})$$

$$s = \int_0^{t_c} r_B \dot{\varphi} dt = \int_{\tilde{\varphi}_0}^{\tilde{\varphi}_c} |\mathbf{P}'_B[x(\psi), y(\psi)]| d\psi \qquad (3.47\text{b})$$

It is worth noting that for the case of a non-slip rolling, $v_r = 0$; thus, from (3.47) the curve lengths, CC_A and CC_B, along their respective osculating circles are equal. Unlike a cylindrical or spherical (engineering) joint which is free to spin about its own axis, bio-joints generally have very limited spinning freedom about its own axis as the contact pair of a bio-joint is typically connected by ligaments and tendons. In the following discussions, we focus on the orientation of two DOFs inclination.

The contact point and the position/orientation of Ω_A can be found using the steps summarized in Table 3.5.

Three examples of contacts between two convex/concave ellipses with/without sliding provide intuitive insights into the kinematics of a typical biological joint. The dimensions used in these examples are summarized in Table 3.6, where a_i and b_i are the major and minor radii of the ellipses. Although ellipses are employed for illustration, this model can be used to analyze contact kinematics of non-uniform shapes because the formulation, (3.40)–(3.47), requires only local geometric properties.

Example 3.4.1 Contact between Ellipses

Figure 3.11 shows three snapshots of the ellipse Ω_A rolling on the (fixed) circle Ω_B, where the solid black ellipse and circle are the contact pair at the initial position ($\tilde{\theta}_0 = 0$). The two consecutive snapshots are graphed in red and blue colors respectively. In Fig. 3.3, the green circles mark the initial contact point on Ω_A; the blue asterisks indicate the current point C; and the dashed circles are the osculating circles at the two respective instants. As shown in Fig. 3.11, the normal vector $\mathbf{e}_N$ (and thus ω_T and its direction) of the boundary Γ_A changes with the contact point.

Table 3.5 Algorithm for bio-joint kinematics

(1) Determine the initial contact position between Ω_A and Ω_B, i.e. $\tilde{\theta}_0$ and $\tilde{\varphi}_0$ in their own local frame
(2) Calculate the increment of s from $r_A(\psi)\omega\Delta t$ (Δt is the time step, for the first step $\psi = \tilde{\theta}_0$)
(3) Find the contact point C on Ω_A by solving

$$s = \int_{\tilde{\theta}_0}^{\tilde{\theta}_c} |d\mathbf{P}_A/d\psi| d\psi \qquad (3.48)$$

(4) To find the contact point C at $t = n\Delta t$ on Ω_A, repeat step 2 and 3 by updating $r_A(\psi)$
(5) Determine point C on Ω_B by solving (3.47b) for $\tilde{\varphi}_c$
(6) Use (3.47) to determine the position/orientation of Ω_A

Table 3.6 Simulation parameter values

$\omega = \pi/12$ rad/s	Ω_A		Ω_B	
	b_1/a_1	a_1 (cm)	b_2/a_2	a_2 (cm)
Dimensions	0.5	2	1	1

Fig. 3.11 Snapshots
illustrating the formulation

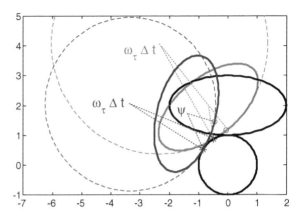

Fig. 3.12 Effect of shapes on
the osculating circle

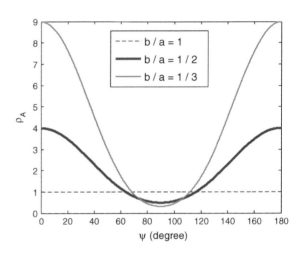

The computation procedure given in Table 3.5 can be illustrated as follows:

(1) As derived in (3.45), the radius of an osculating circle is a function of the contact position. The shape effect of Ω_A on the radius ρ_A is graphed as a function of ψ (or the local angle measured from the major axis characterizing the point on Ω_A) in Fig. 3.11. Unlike a circle ($b/a = 1$), there are osculating circles of different sizes at different points on the ellipse Ω_A.

(2) At $t = \Delta t$ (= 1s), Ω_A (red) rotates by $\omega\Delta t$ with $r_A(0)$, and thus the distance increment $\Delta s = r_A(0)\omega\Delta t$. Then, the contact point on Ω_A can be found by calculating ψ (= $\Delta\psi$) from (3.48):

Fig. 3.13 Ellipse—cylinder contact

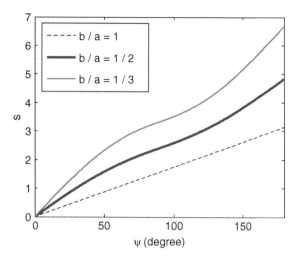

$$\Delta s = \int_0^{\Delta\psi} \left|\frac{d\mathbf{P}_A}{d\psi}\right| d\psi.$$

(3) Similarly, at $t = 2\Delta t$ (= 2s), Ω_A (blue) rotates by an additional $\omega\Delta t$ from the previous contact point with $\rho_A(\Delta\psi)$, and thus the next $\Delta s = \rho_A(\Delta\psi)\omega\Delta t$ and ψ can be obtained from (3.48) with updated integration bounds.

(4) The computed displacement s is given in Fig. 3.13 for different b/a ratios of Ω_A. In Fig. 3.13, $\psi = 0$ corresponds to the orientation when the major axis of Ω_A is horizontal as shown in Fig. 3.11. For a circle, s increases linearly because r_A is a constant; while for an ellipse, s increases nonlinearly with r_A.

Because of no slippage, the contact point moves at the same displacement on Ω_A and Ω_B, and $\tilde{\varphi}_c$ can be solved from (3.47b). Note that $\tilde{\theta}_c$ and $\tilde{\varphi}_c$ are in different local coordinate frames, which must be represented in the same world frame using (3.40) to obtain the position and orientation of Ω_A.

Example 3.4.2 Effect of Sliding on Contact Kinematics

The effect of sliding can be explained using (3.47a). Note that when $v_r = \omega r_A$, $s = 0$; the contact becomes pure sliding. As shown in Fig. 3.12, $\min(r_A)$ occurs at $\psi = 90°$. For simplicity, $v_r = \omega\cdot\min(r_A) = 0.1309$ mm/s is chosen for illustration so that pure sliding occurs at the contact point with the minimal rotation radius. The results simulating the effect of sliding on the same contact pair in Fig. 3.11 (thick solid black ellipse and circle) are given in Figs. 3.14 and 3.15.

Figure 3.14 compares the two consecutive snapshots with sliding contact (thin-line ellipses) against those obtained without slippage (dash-line ellipses). In Fig. 3.14, ellipses of the same color appear at the same instance: black ($t = 0$), red

Fig. 3.14 Effect of sliding on contact kinematics

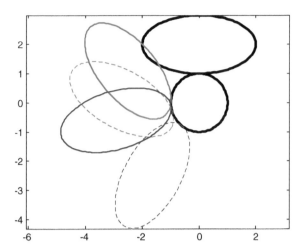

Fig. 3.15 Effect of sliding on orientation

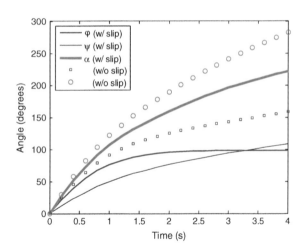

($t = \Delta t = 1$ s) and blue ($t = 2\Delta t = 2$ s). As compared in Fig. 3.14, rolling without slippage moves more than sliding contact as expected.

Figure 3.15 compares the angular displacement φ and the orientation α of the ellipse Ω_A rolling on the circle Ω_B with and without slippage. The non-slip rolling has a larger φ and α. In Fig. 3.15, the angle ψ is independent of the contact conditions. The curves for φ and ψ intersect at $\varphi = \psi = 90°$ for rolling with $v_r = \min(r_A)$. In other words, this instantaneous contact point does not move (and stay at the same position on Ω_B no matter how fast Ω_A rotates). This result can be explained with the aid of (3.47a) and Fig. 3.12 showing $s = 0$ when $v_r = \omega r_A$ and $\min(r_A)$ at $\psi = 90°$ respectively.

Example 3.4.3 Contact between Convex/Concave Ellipses

As an illustration, the orientation (or the rotation angle of the minor axis) of Ω_A and the distance between the two centroids for the four cases are computed and the results are compared in Figs. 3.16 and 3.17. The values used in the simulation are summarized in Table 3.7, where a_i and b_i are the major and minor radii of the ellipses. Some observations, highlighting the differences between the commonly seen engineering joints, Cases 2(a) and 2(b), and the more general bio-joints, Cases 1(a) and 1(b), can be summarized as follows:

(1) The orientation of Ω_A changes nonlinearly for the contact cases of ellipses and linearly for those of circles. In addition, the inclination range of a bio-joint depends on the aspect ratio b_i/a_i.
(2) Unlike a concentric (cylindrical or ball-socket) joint that has negligible clearance between the contacting elements, an elliptical convex-concave contact of a bio-joint has a limited range of orientation movement.
(3) As compared in Fig. 3.17a, the orientation of an elliptical convex-convex joint may be approximated by a circular convex-convex joint within a limited range.

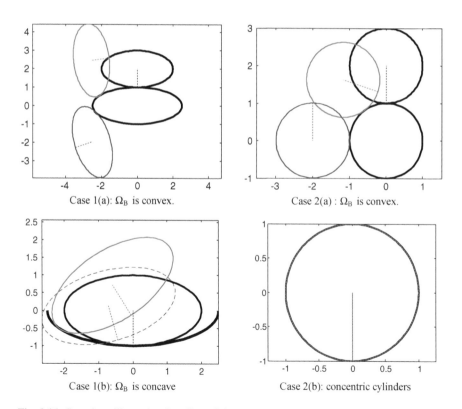

Case 1(a): Ω_B is convex.

Case 2(a) : Ω_B is convex.

Case 1(b): Ω_B is concave

Case 2(b): concentric cylinders

Fig. 3.16 Snapshots illustrating the effect of shape

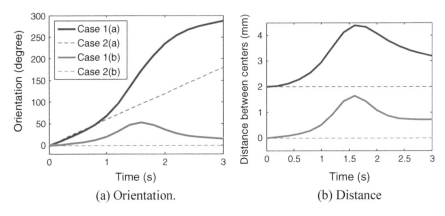

Fig. 3.17 Effect of Ω_B on Ω_A position/orientation

Table 3.7 Dimension of Ω_A and Ω_B

Case	Ω_A (convex)		Ω_B	
	b_1/a_1	a_1 (cm)	b_2/a_2	a_2 (cm)
1(a) and 1(b)	0.5	2	0.4	2.5
2(a) and 2(b)	1	1	1	1

Case (a): Ω_B is convex; and Cases (b): Ω_B is concave. ($\omega = \pi/6$ rad/s)

The validity of the orientation approximation depends on the specific aspect ratios b_i/a_i of the contact pair; see for example, Fig. 3.18 where the circular convex-convex approximation does not work.

Unlike the circular convex-convex joint where the center of Ω_A remains a constant distance from that of Ω_B as shown in Case 2(a) and 2(b) in Figs. 3.16 and 3.17b, the center of Ω_A changes nonlinearly for the cases of an elliptical joint.

3.5 Summary

This chapter has formulated the models for typical types of flexible elements, and the governing equations can be written compactly in the following form

$$\mathbf{X}' = \mathbf{f}(t, \mathbf{X}(t)) \qquad (3.1a)$$

where t is the independent variable, $\mathbf{X}$ is the vector of state variables that are summarized as follows

(3.4) for a 2D beam $t = s$, $\mathbf{X}(s) = [u \, w \, \theta F_1 F_3 M_2]^T$

(3.12) for a 3D beam $t = s$, $\mathbf{X}(s) = [R_{11}R_{12}R_{13}x_1x_2x_3\varphi \, F_1F_2F_3M_1M_2M_3]^T$

Fig. 3.18 Effect of aspect ratio

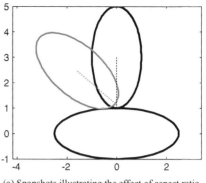

(a) Snapshots illustrating the effect of aspect ratio

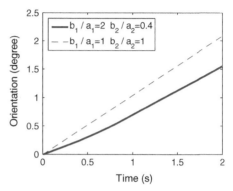

(b) Ω_A orientation as a function of time

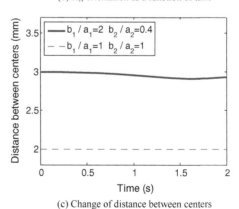

(c) Change of distance between centers

(3.32) for an annular plate $t = R$, $\mathbf{X}(R) = \left[\Phi_{nm} \; \Phi_{nm}'' \; \Phi_{nm}'' \; \Phi_{nm}''' \right]^{\mathrm{T}}$.

The boundary conditions (3.1b) are formulated for each of the elements in different cases, and the boundary value problems are investigated for illustrative applications. The application of the flexible beam is demonstrated with a flexonic mobile node for structural health monitoring in Chap. 4. Intelligent sensing for manufacturing thin-wall components is employed as an example of the annular plate model in Chap. 5. The general constraint is formulated with simulation algorithms to emulate the constraints in biological joints, which will be detailed in Chaps. 6 and 7.

References

1. A.H. Nayfeh, P.P. Frank, *Linear and Nonlinear Structural Mechanics* (Wiley, Hoboken, New Jersey, USA, 2008)
2. H.W. Guggenheimer, *Differential Geometry* (Dover Publications, New York, 1977)
3. J. Stoer, R. Bulirsch, *Introduction to Numerical Analysis* (Springer, New York, 1993)

Chapter 4
Flexonic Mobile Node

This chapter will apply the beam modeling method to develop a flexible robot, namely flexonic mobile node (FMN), which is capable of obstacle negotiation and data collection on complicated structures with the help of compliant beam deformations. The remainder of this chapter starts with the design concept of FMN and continues with simulated analysis for functionalities, then experimental validation and illustrative examples will be presented for structural health monitoring.

4.1 Design Concept

Figure 4.1 shows a network of autonomous robots, which are capable of carrying smart sensors and navigating on civil structures for health monitoring. Each robot is featured with small size, magnetic attachment and compliant mechatronics. Its front axle and rear axle are connected by a compliant beam, through which it can load/unload a sensor on the working surface and negotiate corners with various poses, so it is named as the flexonic mobile node (FMN). Operating with onboard batteries and communicating wirelessly, the FMNs do not require external cables for power or communication. The wireless sensing unit serves as the "brain" of each FMN, and performs various tasks such as analog signal sampling, data processing, motor control, and wireless communication between the central server and its peers.

As civil structures are built with established engineering criterions and standards, a field robot to navigate on these structures should be designed under certain guidelines, which can be categorized into the following topics of dimensions, attachment and flexibility. Along the discussion of these guidelines, the design concepts of the FMN are also delivered.

© Huazhong University of Science and Technology Press, Wuhan and Springer Nature Singapore Pte Ltd. 2019
J. Guo and K.-M Lee, *Flexonics for Manufacturing and Robotics*, Research on Intelligent Manufacturing, https://doi.org/10.1007/978-981-13-2667-7_4

Fig. 4.1 Flexonic mobile node for structural health monitoring

4.1.1 Dimension

Dimension of a field robot is obviously critical to its design of mechanical and electrical components. However, it is even more important to the function of obstacle avoidance. Figure 4.2 shows a schematic of a general robot (either wheeled or legged) to overcome an obstacle, where the featured dimensions of the robot and the obstacle are denoted as R and H, respectively. In this way, the robot can be considered as a sphere of radius R, and it is subjected to a virtual pushing force F from motors or actuators. When the force can provide enough positive torque $F(R - H)$, the robot can overcome the obstacle. In this way, if R is much larger than H, it is very easy to climb the step as shown in Fig. 4.2a. However, if R is close to H, or in other words, the robot is about the same size as an obstacle, it tends to be trapped as shown in Fig. 4.2b. Also, if R is much smaller than H, then the task can be divided into a sequence of typical obstacle avoidance motions, such as negotiating concave and convex corners in Fig. 4.2c. Of course, an attaching force would be required for certain motions, such as climbing, to compensate for the gravity.

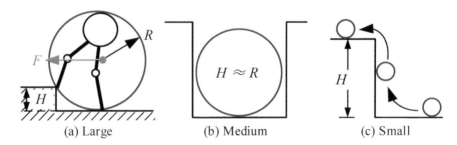

     (a) Large   (b) Medium   (c) Small

Fig. 4.2 Robot dimension compared to obstacles

With typical obstacles in mind, it is reasonable to design a robot either much larger or much smaller than the featured dimension of obstacles. For SHM, an extremely big robot would be too heavy, energy inefficient and risky. Since the width and length of general trusses is larger than 15 and 200 cm, one axle of the FMN is designed as compact as about 8 cm × 8 cm × 8 cm. In this way, navigation on complicated truss structures can be achieved with strategies developed for overcoming simple obstacles of convex and concave corners.

4.1.2 Attachment

Permanent magnets are employed to provide attraction forces to attach the FMN onto an iron surface. The novel concept of the fixed magnet configuration is developed from the general design of alternative rotating magnets. Figure 4.3a shows one of the traditional magnetic wheels, where thin rectangular magnets envelop a solid cylinder with their magnetization axes arranged alternatively pointing towards and outwards from the wheel center. However, the new configuration fixes the magnet on the frame (Fig. 4.3b), so that the robot moves with the externally rotating wheel by only compensating for the friction; while in the design of rotating magnets, the wheel embodies a polygon profile and the driving force has to compensate for the magnetic force, which is much larger than the friction. As the polygon wheel moves on a surface, its center vibrates vertically because of the varying rotation radius. This dynamics contributes to the tilting of the robot frame body (Fig. 4.3b), which deteriorates the performance of the onboard sensors such as the image processing unit. In this way, the supporting columns have to be added to maintain the frame orientation. But the fixed magnet configuration can naturally maintain its pose in a similar manner as a tumbler, thus can perform much smoother motions.

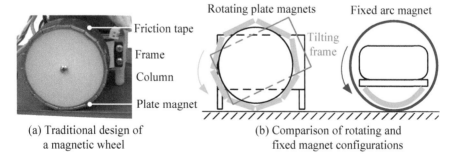

(a) Traditional design of
a magnetic wheel

(b) Comparison of rotating and
fixed magnet configurations

Fig. 4.3 Comparison of two magnetic wheel configurations

4.1.3 Flexibility

A field robot is desired to be as flexible as possible to negotiate various types of obstacles, implying the more degrees-of-freedom (DOFs) the better. A four-wheel robot is used as a comparison platform for different design configurations. Assuming the robot is self-balanced with fixed magnets as proposed in the previous section, the rear axle embodies 2 DOFs as it can move forward/backward and make turns on a plane. In the following, the front-axle relative motion is analyzed for four design configurations and their total DOFs are summarized in Table 4.1:

– *DC1 (Link)*: When connected with a rigid link, the front axle has no relative motion with respect to the rear axle.
– *DC2 (Pin joint)*: The added pin joint allows the front axle to rotate with respect to the rear axle. The rotation direction depends on the pin axis orientation.
– *DC3 (Ball joint)*: The front axle is able to rotate in the 3D space with a ball joint characterized by yawing, pitching and rolling. However, the rotation range is limited, and the distance between the front and rear axles is uniquely determined once the front axle orientation is known.
– *DC4 (Compliant beam)*: By connecting with a compliant beam subject to both bending and twisting, the front axle is capable of both rotation and translation in the 3D space, and the rotation range is much larger than DC3. It is noted that the compliant beam can have infinite number of deformed shapes, which has not been accounted in this analysis.

Figure 4.4 illustrates the design concept of an FMN consisting of four independently driven magnetic wheels housed in two assemblies (front and rear) connected by a compliant beam. Unlike a rigid car frame with a fixed distance between the front and rear axles, the front axle of an FMN can be bent relatively to its rear axle by deforming the compliant beam (with both of its ends fixed on the two rigid bodies at P_0 and P_1). This enables the FMN not only to function as an agile locomotion but also a sensor loader. It can be easily noticed that definitions of coordinate frames here are the same as in Fig. 3.3. It is recalled that the local coordinate frames, "xyz" and "$\xi\eta\zeta$" (each with a subscript indicating its location

Table 4.1 Comparison of degrees of freedom

DC 1	DC 2	DC 3	DC 4
F			
R			
DOF = 2	DOF = 3	DOF = 5	DOF = 8

along the beam path-length), are defined in the un-deformed and deformed configurations respectively. The nodal displacements u_s, v_s and w_s are along x_s, y_s and z_s axis directions respectively. When the beam cross section is rectangular, all the coordinates follow the right-hand rule with x_s and ξ_s assigned along the neutral axis of the beam, and z_s and ζ_s normal to the beam surface.

4.2 Functionalities

The functionalities of an FMN are achieved with a compliant beam connecting the front and rear axles as shown in Fig. 4.4, so the formulated beam models are best illustrated by numerically simulating the basic functions of the FMN, where parametric values for the beam models are listed in Table 4.2.

(1) The first function attaches or detaches an accelerometer on/from the surface to be measured. The compliant beam is normally straight. When a measurement is to be made, the front axle is driven toward the rear axle to buckle the compliant beam allowing the accelerometer to be pressed against the surface to be measured.

(2) The second function provides a means to overcome obstacles when moving on a structure. Among the challenges is negotiating sharp corners. The magnetic forces decrease greatly when negotiating a convex corner, but they increase (because of multiple contacts) when moving up or down a concave corner.

(3) The third function offers a sensing platform to monitor the environments. The camera on the front axle is tilted by manipulating the compliant beam, thus environmental information can be captured via machine vision.

Fig. 4.4 Design concept of an FMN

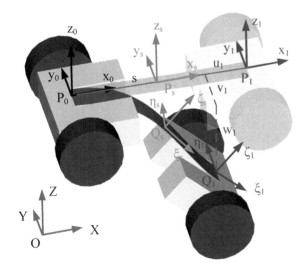

Table 4.2 Mechanical properties and thickness of the spring steel laminate

Elastic modulus E (GPa)	207	Density ρ (g/cm^3)	7.63
Shear modulus G (GPa)	79.3	Thickness h (mm)	0.254
Poisson ratio υ	0.3		

4.2.1 Sensor Attachment

In modeling the sensor attachment on a plane, the rear axle is treated as a fixed end, and the front axle acts as a slider subjected to a uni-axial loading F_1 as shown in Fig. 4.5. In addition, it is assumed that the compliant beam is constrained to bend only in the $-z$ direction. For a given wheel radius, the uniaxial loading F_1 required to move the sensor to its desired displacement w_s (at $s = 1/2$) depends on the direction of the sensor displacement relative to gravity as compared in Fig. 4.5, which compares two cases. Unlike Case 1 where the weights of the sensor and beam facilitate the sensor attachment, the beam must compensate for these weights in Case 2. To explain the effect of the gravity, the specified force F_1 is normalized to the critical buckling force for a beam subjected to both ends fixed [1] as follows:

Fig. 4.5 Effect of gravity

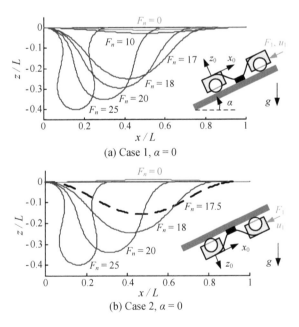

(a) Case 1, $\alpha = 0$

(b) Case 2, $\alpha = 0$

$$F_n = F_1 \left(\frac{4L^2}{\pi^2 EI_2} \right) \tag{4.1}$$

The sensor gravity normalized using (4.1) is about 0.8. With type-3 BC in Table 3.1, the deformed shape (or w as a function of path length s) and $u_1 = x_1 - x_1^{(0)}$ for specified F_1 can be computed by solving the BVP (3.1) with the 2D beam model. The results for the two cases (with $\alpha = 0$) are compared in Figs. 4.5 and 4.6 where the input force F_n varies from 0 to 25.

Some observations are discussed as follows:

- Figures 4.5a and 4.6a show that the beam deforms continuously as the normalized force increases in Case 1.
- Although the carrying mass (50 g sensor) is relatively light causing negligible deformation under its own weight (see red curves in Fig. 4.5, $F_1 = 0$), this little weight, however, has a significant buckling effect on the beam in Case 2. As illustrated in Figs. 4.5b and 4.6a, both the displacements (u_1 and w_s) in Case 2 do not change until the normalized force exceeds a critical value F_{nc} at which the beam buckles drastically to a new shape (see black dash curve in Fig. 4.6b) without any intermediate shapes. The values of u_1 and w_s, which correspond to F_{nc} for $\alpha = 0°$, $45°$, $90°$, are summarized in Table 4.3, which also shows the effects of sensor weights on these values. These critical values that cause buckling to set off in Case 2 decrease (requiring less compensation against gravity) as α increases. For the same reason, a heavier weight tends to give rise to a larger critical value for $\alpha < 45°$. On other hand, a smaller critical value for a heavier weight for $\alpha > 45°$ is observed as gravity facilitates buckling.
- For $\alpha = 90°$, the theoretical value of 16 given in [1] for a weightless beam is somewhat larger than F_{nc} of 15.5. The beam model given in (3.4) accounts for the gravity along $-x$, which contributes to the onset of buckling.
- The values of w_s for different α values converge to the case $\alpha = 90°$ for large F_1 when the gravity becomes negligible. This is also true for u_1 because of the monotonous relation between w_s and u_1 as shown in Fig. 4.6b. The maximum normalized force required is $F_n = 25$, from which the required motor torque can be estimated by multiplying F_1 computed from (4.1) by the wheel radius r_w.
- The solution to the beam model provides two alternative manipulating variables (F_1 or u_1) of controlling w_s for attaching a sensor. As illustrated in Fig. 4.6a, the relationship between F_1 and w_s is not only highly nonlinear, but also depends on α. On the other hand, the relationship between w_s and u_1 is monotonically smooth and independent of α, as shown in Fig. 4.6b. Thus, it is a preferable variable for controlling the compliant beam of the FMN by manipulating the input displacement u_1 rather than the input force F_1. The inverse model that computes u_1 for a specified w_s for attaching sensor is given by curve fitting the data in Fig. 4.6b for different α's in both cases

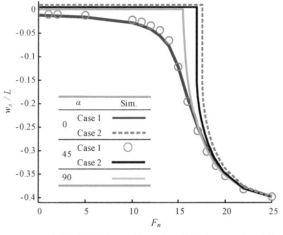

(a) Relation between force F_n and displacement w_s / L

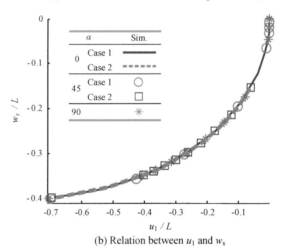

(b) Relation between u_1 and w_s

Fig. 4.6 Relationship between normalized force and displacements

Table 4.3 Slope angle and critical values

Sensor gravity (normalized)	α (degree)	F_{nc}	u_1/L	w_s/L
0.8	0	17.5	−0.0624	0.1559
	45	16.9	−0.0612	0.1543
	90	15.5	−0.0002	0.0094
1.6	0	18.3	−0.0999	0.1948
	45	17.3	−0.1069	0.2009
	90	15.1	−0.00005	0.0001

$$\frac{u_1}{L} = 18\left(\frac{w_s}{L}\right)^3 + 5.3\left(\frac{w_s}{L}\right)^2 - 0.85\frac{w_s}{L} \tag{4.2}$$

This result is due to the light weight of the combined beam and sensor. For detaching a sensor, the command becomes $-u_1$ for a reversed process.

4.2.2 Convex Corner Negotiation (2D)

Figure 4.7 shows the free body diagram of the front assembly (mass m_1 at mass center C_1 and wheel radius r_w) at an instant crossing a convex corner A. The reference OXYZ is defined such that X axis is on the plane, where the FMN initially locates and points in the moving direction before crossing the corner, and Z axis is normal to the plane. In Fig. 4.7, α is the angle between Z axis and the gravity, F_N is the reaction force, $f(=\mu F_N)$ is the friction, μ is the coefficient of friction between the wheel and surface, and M_m is the torque provided by the motors.

The following discussion considers the worst scenario where the wheel has a point contact at the corner, and the following assumptions are made in this discussion:

(1) The wheels are designed with magnets such that they attach on the steel surfaces as the FMN moves.
(2) The motor torque satisfies the non-slip condition: $M_m = f r_w \leq \mu F_N(\theta) r_w$
(3) The moment due to the magnets is small as compared to that due to gravity, and thus neglected in the analysis.

The strategy for an FMN to negotiate a convex corner comprises three steps:

Step 1: The rear axle exerts the forces/torque (F_x, F_z, and M_y) through the compliant beam to rotate the front axle about A.

Fig. 4.7 Convex corner negotiation

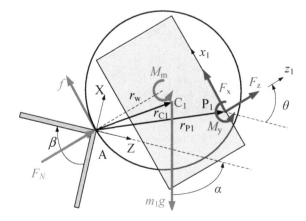

Fig. 4.8 Simulation of corner negotiation

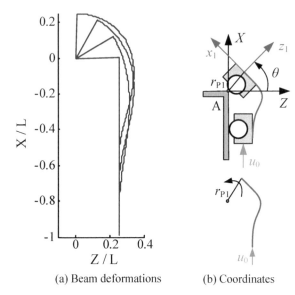

(a) Beam deformations   (b) Coordinates

Step 2: As soon as the front axle crosses over the corner ($\theta = \beta$ where β is the corner angle), the two assemblies move together.

Step 3: Once the rear axle arrives at the corner, the front axle pulls it over via the compliant beam.

The following details *Step* 1 as this initiation dictates the success of the corner negotiation. Figure 4.8 shows the beam deformations as the front assembly crosses the corner. As will be shown, the other steps follow similar principles.

To rotate the front assembly over the corner, the following condition with respect to point A must be satisfied,

$$M_r \mathbf{E}_2 + \mathbf{r}_{C_1} \times m_1 \mathbf{g} \geq 0 \tag{4.3}$$

where $M_r \mathbf{E}_2 = \mathbf{r}_{P_1} \times (F_x \mathbf{E}_1 + F_z \mathbf{E}_3) + M_y \mathbf{E}_2$ is the required moment to compensate for the torque due to gravity, and it is shown in Fig. 4.9 for different α values.

For negative α, M_r can be obtained from the mirror images of Fig. 4.9. Since the compliant beam attaches the front assembly at P_1,

$$F_x = -F_1, \quad F_z = -F_3, \quad M_y = -M_2 \tag{4.4a, b, c}$$

The BCs (M_2, u and w) for negotiating a convex corner, which take the form of type 4 in Table 3.1, can be obtained from (4.5a) and (4.5b):

$$M_2 = -\mathbf{E}_2 \cdot \mathbf{r}_{P_1} \times (F_1 \mathbf{E}_1 + F_3 \mathbf{E}_3) - M_r \tag{4.5a}$$

$$[u \quad w] = [\mathbf{E}_1 \quad \mathbf{E}_3] \begin{bmatrix} \cos\theta & -\sin\theta \\ \sin\theta & \cos\theta \end{bmatrix} \mathbf{r}_{P_1} \tag{4.5b}$$

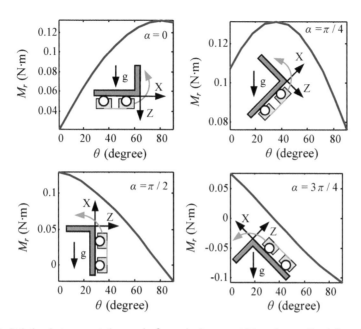

Fig. 4.9 Relation between rotation angle θ, required moment M_r and normalized force F_n

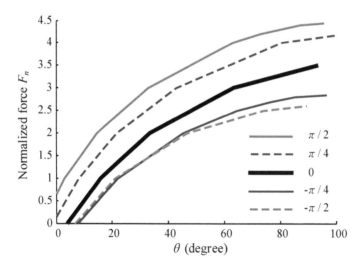

Fig. 4.10 Relation between rotation angle α and normalized force F_n

Solving (3.4) with (4.5) as constraints using MSM, the simulation results are given in Fig. 4.10 showing the highly nonlinear relationship between θ and the applied force (for α equal to 0, $\pm\pi/4$, $\pm\pi/2$). The larger the α, the larger the force required for a desired rotation angle, and the maximum normalized force is about 4.5 (smaller than the maximum force of 25 for sensor attachment).

4.2.3 Convex Corner Negotiation (3D)

Figure 4.11 shows an FMN at an instant crossing a convex corner A from Plane I to Plane II. The reference frame XYZ is defined such that axis Z is normal to the plane I where the FMN initially locates and axis X is normal to the corner edge. Similarly, the frame X'Y'Z' is obtained by rotating the frame XYZ with respect to the axis Y so that Z' is normal to the plane II. Because of limited turning space, the FMN changes its initially aligned front and rear axles by turning the front assembly (equivalent to a rigid body with mass m_1 and mass center C_1, and the wheel radius is r_w) and deforming the compliant beam. The coordinate frames $P_0x_0y_0z_0$ and $P_1x_1y_1z_1$ are attached to the beam rear and front ends, where x_0 and x_1 are along the beam axis while z_0 and z_1 are normal to the beam surface, so they characterize positions and orientations of both ends, respectively.

The strategy for the FMN to negotiate a 3D convex corner with limited turning space comprises three steps:

Step 1: The rear axle turns so that the front axle can approach the edge perpendicularly, where ψ is the angle between X and x_0. Afterwards, the rear axle pushes forwards by u_0 along x_0, exerting forces F_1 and torque M_1 through the compliant beam to rotate the front axle about A by θ which is determined by the angle formed by the axes Z and z_1.

Step 2: Right after the front axle crosses over the corner, the two axles move together.

Step 3: As soon as the rear axle reaches the corner, it is pulled over by the front axle via the compliant beam.

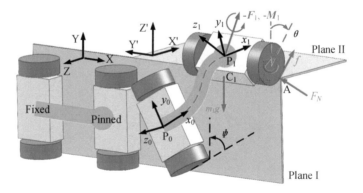

Fig. 4.11 Turning within a limited space

Step 1 is detailed in the following as the success of the convex corner negotiation in the 3D space is dictated by this initiation, which differs from the 2D case as presented in the previous section. In Fig. 4.11, F_N is the normal force acting on both wheels of the front axle; $f(=\mu F_N)$ is the friction; μ is the coefficient of friction between the wheel and the ground; and M_m is the torque provided by the front axle motors. The following assumptions are made in this discussion:

(1) The wheels are designed with the fixed magnet configuration (Fig. 4.3b) so that the FMN is attached on the steel surfaces as it moves.
(2) The non-slip condition is satisfied:

$$M_m = f r_w \leq \mu F_N(\theta) r_w \qquad (4.6)$$

(3) Because the magnets are very close to the surface, the moment arm is very small, thus the magnetic torque is negligible as compared to that due to gravity.

For the front assembly to cross the corner, the inequality (4.7) must be satisfied with respect to A:

$$|M_r \mathbf{i}_{Y'} + \mathbf{r}_{C_1} \times m_1 \mathbf{g}| \geq 0 \qquad (4.7)$$

where $M_r \mathbf{i}_{Y'} = -\mathbf{r}_{P_1} \times \mathbf{F}_1 - \mathbf{M}_1$ is the required moment to compensate for the gravitational torque, $\mathbf{i}_Y$ is a unit vector along the Y axis, $\mathbf{r}_{C1}$ and $\mathbf{r}_{P1}$ are the projected arm lengths of AC_1 and AP_1 on the plane XZ. The BCs for negotiating a 3D convex corner, which take the form of Type 4 in Table 3.2, can be obtained from (4.8a, 4.8b):

$$\mathbf{M}_1 = \mathbf{r}_{C_1} \times m_1 \mathbf{g} - \mathbf{r}_{P_1} \times \mathbf{F}_1 \qquad (4.8a)$$

$$[x_1 \, y_1 \, z_1]^T = [L \, 0 \, 0]^T + [\mathbf{R}_\psi]([\mathbf{R}_\theta]^T - [\mathbf{I}])\mathbf{r}_{P1} \qquad (4.8b)$$

where

$$[\mathbf{R}_\theta] = \begin{bmatrix} \cos\theta & 0 & -\sin\theta \\ 0 & 1 & 0 \\ \sin\theta & 0 & \cos\theta \end{bmatrix}, \quad [\mathbf{R}_\psi] = \begin{bmatrix} \cos\psi & -\sin\psi & 0 \\ \sin\psi & \cos\psi & 0 \\ 0 & 0 & 1 \end{bmatrix}.$$

It is noted that the above equations are formulated in vector forms, so they are valid for any direction the FMN moves towards relative to the gravity. Solving (3.14) with (4.8) as constraints using MSM, the results are given in Figs. 4.12 and 4.13 showing the deformed beam shapes and the highly nonlinear relationship between θ and the applied force/displacement:

– Fig. 4.12 shows the snapshots of the deformed beam at different rotation angle θ, suggesting that large deformations of both bending and twisting occur on the beam. In simulating the corner negotiation, the rear axle pushes the front axle along the x_0 direction while maintaining ψ at a constant value of 60° so that the input force or displacement of the rear axle is along x_0.

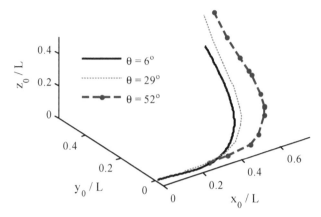

(a) Snapshots of the deformed beam axis

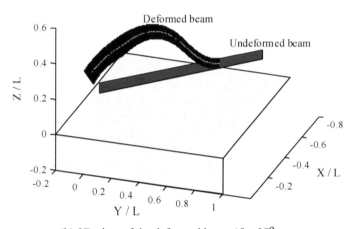

(b) 3D view of the deformed beam ($\theta = 27°$)

Fig. 4.12 Snapshots of the deformed beam

– In Fig. 4.13, the normalized input force and displacement appear to be linear
when $\theta \leq 45°$. When $\theta > 45°$, the inputs start to grow nonlinearly, implying
certain geometry constraints may prevent the front axle to rotate further without
extremely large forces. The displacement u_0 is given by:

$$\frac{u_0}{L} = \begin{cases} 0.0036\theta & \text{if } \theta \leq 45° \\ 0.0016\theta^2 - 0.1431\theta + 3.3292 & \text{if } \theta > 45° \end{cases} \quad (4.9)$$

In this way, the constant ψ strategy is invalid; in other words, the rear axle has to
adaptively increase ψ as it approaches the corner edge in the perpendicular
direction.

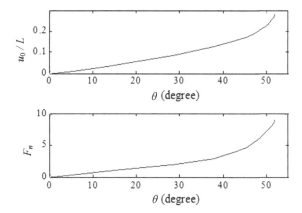

Fig. 4.13 Normalized displacement and force

– Finally, the input-output relationship for 3D corner negotiation within the limited space can be implemented as open-loop control in real time using (4.9). For a closed-loop control, the displacement/orientation feedback can be achieved but requires additional sensors (such as rotary encoders or gyroscope).

4.2.4 Concave Corner Negotiation

Compared to the 3-step strategy to negotiate a convex corner within a limited space, concave corner negotiation is much simpler because it is automated in nature by the fixed magnet configuration as illustrated in Fig. 4.3b. Considering only one axle approaching the corner on the plane I as shown in Fig. 4.14, it is driven by the motor torque M_m as given by (4.6). Once the wheels push against the plane II, the axle could not move any further and the wheels get stuck (Fig. 4.14a). As the wheels do not rotate, the frame would be subjected to the reaction torque from the wheels, which is equal to $-M_m$. Although the magnetic forces are very large to attach the robot to any iron surface, the magnetic torque is actually smaller than the motor torque, thus the frame starts to rotate as shown in Fig. 4.14b. After the magnets get released from the plane I and attracted to the plane II, the axle can continue moving and the task of concave corner negotiation is achieved in Fig. 4.14c.

4.2.5 Environment Monitoring

As the FMN navigates on civil structures, it is necessary to monitor its surrounding environment for navigation decisions and data collection. With a camera implemented on the front axle, it is desired to control the front-axle orientation (ψ and θ) as described in its body-fixed frame $\{\mathbf{e}_{1f}, \mathbf{e}_{2f}, \mathbf{e}_{3f}\}$ as shown in Fig. 4.15. Yaw

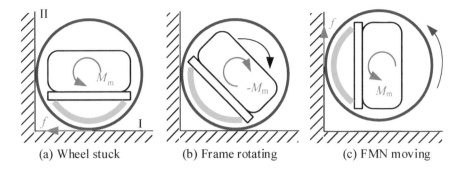

(a) Wheel stuck   (b) Frame rotating   (c) FMN moving

Fig. 4.14 Concave corner negotiation

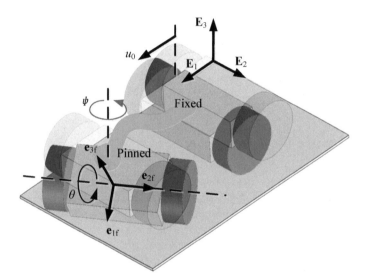

Fig. 4.15 Front axle yawing and pitching

of the front axle is controlled by the difference between the rotational speeds of its left and right wheels when releasing the pin joint on the front axle. On the other hand, as indicated in the previous analysis, pitch of the front axle is controlled by manipulating the compliant beam via the rear axle displacement u_0. So this section will investigate the relation between u_0 and θ with different values of ψ.

Relation between $\{e_{1f}, e_{2f}, e_{3f}\}$ and the global reference frame is given by

$$
\begin{Bmatrix} \mathbf{e}_{1f} \\ \mathbf{e}_{2f} \\ \mathbf{e}_{3f} \end{Bmatrix} = \mathbf{R}_\theta \mathbf{R}_\psi \begin{Bmatrix} \mathbf{E}_1 \\ \mathbf{E}_2 \\ \mathbf{E}_3 \end{Bmatrix} \tag{4.10}
$$

where

$$\mathbf{R}_\psi = \begin{bmatrix} \cos\psi & \sin\psi & 0 \\ -\sin\psi & \cos\psi & 0 \\ 0 & 0 & 1 \end{bmatrix} \text{ and } \mathbf{R}_\theta = \begin{bmatrix} \cos\theta & 0 & -\sin\theta \\ 0 & 1 & 0 \\ \sin\theta & 0 & \cos\theta \end{bmatrix}.$$

Then the position of the beam attaching point on the front axle is given by

$$\mathbf{x}_{P1} = x_i\mathbf{E}_i = r_w\theta\mathbf{e}_{1f} + \mathbf{r}_{P1}^\mathrm{T}(\mathbf{R}_\theta\mathbf{R}_\psi - \mathbf{I}) + L\mathbf{E}_1$$

where the first term is the front-axle motion from pure wheel-rolling, the second term is due to the rigid body rotation with $\mathbf{r}_{P1} = [d_1\ 0\ d_3]^\mathrm{T}$ being the beam attaching position on the front axle expressed in the frame $\{\mathbf{e}_{1f}, \mathbf{e}_{2f}, \mathbf{e}_{3f}\}$, and the third term is expressed in terms of the initial straight beam length. Then the components of $\mathbf{x}_{P1}$ in the global reference frame can be expressed as

$$\begin{aligned} x_1 &= L + r\theta\cos\psi + [d_1(-1 + \cos\theta) + d_3\sin\theta]\cos\psi \\ y_1 &= r\theta\sin\psi + [d_1(-1 + \cos\theta) + d_3\sin\theta]\sin\psi \\ z_1 &= d_3(-1 + \cos\theta) - d_1\sin\theta \end{aligned} \tag{4.11}$$

Different from the previous analysis of corner negotiation, the magnetic torque here becomes dominant over the gravitational torque. Based on the equilibrium of the front axle in the $\mathbf{e}_{2f}$ direction

$$\tau_m\mathbf{e}_{2f} = (r_w\mathbf{E}_3 + \mathbf{r}_{P1}) \times \mathbf{F} + \mathbf{M} \tag{4.12}$$

where $\tau_m = -k_\theta\,\theta$ is the magnetic torque with equivalent rotational spring constant k_θ, $\mathbf{F}\ (=F_1\mathbf{E}_1)$ and $\mathbf{M}\ (=M_1\mathbf{E}_1 + M_2\mathbf{E}_2 + M_3\mathbf{E}_3)$ are the force and moment exerted by the beam, respectively. From (4.10) and (4.12), the moment from the beam can be obtained as

$$\begin{aligned} M_1 &= k_\theta\theta\sin\psi \\ M_2 &= F_1(r_w + d_z) - k_\theta\theta\cos\psi \\ M_3 &= 0 \end{aligned} \tag{4.13}$$

In the above, the pitch angle θ is determined from the orientation of the beam attachment on the front axle. It is noted that $[\mathbf{R}]_1 = [R_{11}\ R_{12}\ R_{13}]$ in (2.19) is the tangential vector along the beam axis, and it lies in the plane of formed by $\mathbf{e}_{1f}$ and $\mathbf{e}_{2f}$. Then $\mathbf{e}_{3f}$ is given by $[\mathbf{R}]_1 \times \mathbf{e}_{2f}$. Considering (4.10), θ is determined as follows

$$\sin\theta = -R_{13}, \quad \cos\theta = R_{11}\cos\psi + R_{12}\sin\psi \tag{4.14a, b}$$

By specifying the yaw angle ψ and the pushing force F_1, the pitch angle θ and the rear axle position/displacement (assuming it starts from the origin of the global reference frame, $u_0 = x_1|_{s=0}$) can be obtained by solving the BVP (3.14) with the boundary conditions determined as

$$s = 0: \quad R_{11} = 1, R_{12} = R_{13} = \varphi = 0; \quad x_2 = x_3 = 0; \quad F_1$$
$$s = L: \quad x_1, x_2, x_3, M_1, M_2, M_3$$

which are given by (4.11) and (4.13).

Numerical values of parameters used in the simulation are listed in Tables 4.2 and 4.4.

Figure 4.16 shows the deformed beam shapes for different combinations of ψ and θ. The beam deformation is 2D for $\psi = 0$ and 3D for $\psi \neq 0$. It is noted that the beam deformations for $\psi > 0$ and $\psi < 0$ are symmetric, so only the case of $\psi > 0$ is presented. Besides, for $\theta < 0$ it requires the rear axle to push forwards ($u_0 > 0$) while for $\theta > 0$ the rear axle has to pull backwards ($u_0 < 0$).

Figure 4.17 shows the required input (force F_1 or displacement u_0) of the rear axle to tilt the front axle for different values of ψ and θ. The black circles denote the simulated results and the interpolated surfaces of F_1 (ψ, θ) and u_0 (ψ, θ) can be quantified as follows:

Table 4.4 Parametric values for simulation

k_θ	d_1	d_3
0.69 N m/radian	−21.79 mm	7.11 mm

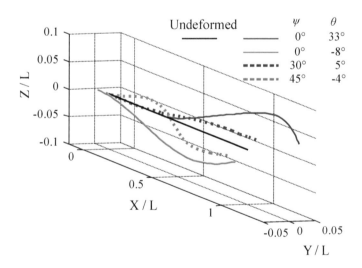

Fig. 4.16 Deformed beam shapes for a pitching camera

Fig. 4.17 Required input of
the rear axle for different of ψ
and θ

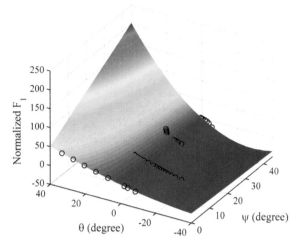

(a) Normalized force from the rear axle

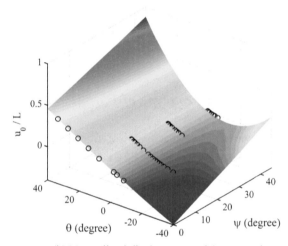

(b) Normalized displacement of the rear axle

$$F_1 \frac{4L^2}{\pi^2 EI_2} = -0.15\theta + 54.54|\psi| + 147.32\theta|\psi| + 27.28\psi^2 + 182.01\theta\psi^2 + 2.50\theta^3$$

$$(4.15a)$$

$$\frac{u_0}{L} = -0.0067\theta + 0.61|\psi| - 0.17\theta|\psi| + 0.07\psi^2 + 1.34\theta\psi^2 + 0.015\theta^3 \quad (4.15b)$$

Results are discussed as follows:

– The input force F_1 is a nonlinear function of ψ and θ. Given an electric motor,
  the maximum output torque M_m can be found from its specification sheet. Then

the limits on the front axle tilting motion can be determined from $|F_1| \leq 2M_m/r_w$.

- For $\psi = 0$, u_0 is a linear function of θ which is similar to the case of corner negotiation as will be seen in Sect. 4.3.2. As ψ increases, u_0 becomes nonlinear with θ because the beam deformation becomes 3D and twisting along the beam axis is nonzero. However, u_0 is still the preferred control variable because displacement control is much more straight forward than force control.

- The surface functions of (4.15) are obtained by multiple variable regression, where the functional form is determined such that they are even functions of ψ (because of symmetry) and odd functions of θ because $F_1 > 0$, $u_0 > 0$ for $\theta > 0$ and $F_1 < 0$, $u_0 < 0$ for $\theta < 0$.

4.3 Experimental Validation

Two FMN prototypes are developed with different magnetic-wheel configurations as indicated in Fig. 4.3, and experimental validation of the functionalities is presented for each of them.

4.3.1 First Prototype of FMN

A prototype FMN that has two (front and rear) wheel assemblies is shown in Fig. 4.18a. Each assembly has a pair of magnetic wheels (independently driven by electric motors), a microprocessor-based pulse width modulation controller, and wireless communication circuits. The dimensions of the FMN is 22.9 cm in length, 15.2 cm in width and 9.1 cm in height. The overall weight of the FMN is 1 kg contributed primarily by the magnets, motors, and batteries. Details of the frame structure and compliant beam are given in Fig. 4.18b, c. As illustrated in Fig. 4.18b, the main body of FMN consists of two U-shaped structural frames on which the motors and electronics are housed and a spring steel (0.254 mm thick) laminate including a compliant beam (shaded in gray). The non-shaded portions are fastened by screws onto the U-shaped frames. The accelerometer (50 g) is pinned in the middle of the beam by screws (at locations shaded in black). Specifications of the spring steel laminate are given in Fig. 4.18c and Table 4.2. The beam has non-uniform cross-sections; thus A and I are functions of s.

The wheels of the FMN are enveloped by thin magnets (with magnetization axes arranged alternately pointing towards and outwards from the wheel center) to provide attraction for climbing on ferromagnetic structures. A Hall-effect sensor is fixed above each magnet wheel for measuring the periodical change of the magnetic flux as the wheel rotates, which provides wheel velocity feedback for real-time control. For the FMN to move (forward or backward) safely on the underlying

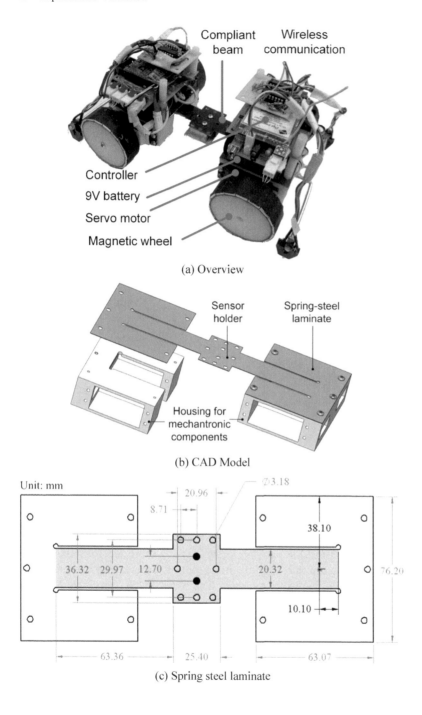

(a) Overview

(b) CAD Model

(c) Spring steel laminate

Fig. 4.18 The first prototype FMN

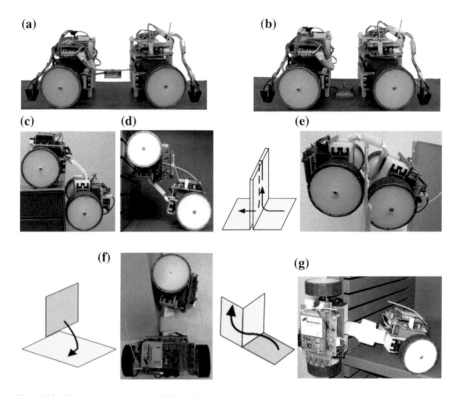

Fig. 4.19 Sensor attachment and obstacle negotiation

structural surface, infrared (IR) sensors are placed at both sides of the front and rear 2-wheel cars for surface boundary detection. When an IR sensor moves outside the surface boundary, changes can be captured from the reduced strength of the reflected IR signal, so that the movement direction can be immediately corrected through motor control.

The beam is mainly designed to attach/detach an accelerometer (see Fig. 4.19a, b) by bending, as well as negotiate corners (see Fig. 4.19c, d) and reinforcement ridges (see Fig. 4.19e). Although the beam can be subjected to some limited twisting that would allow the FMN to move out-of-plane to another surface, as illustrated in Fig. 4.19f, g, results discussed here focus on two functional examples (see Sect. 4.2) that require only 2D bending.

The objectives of the experiments are as follows:

(1) The first objective is to validate the beam model (that reduces the problem from 2D to 1D depending only on the path length s) by comparing against experiments and those computed using FEA. To achieve this objective, the spring-steel laminate alone was used (with one U-shape frame for fixation) so that the complexities of the front and rear assemblies can be avoided.

(2) The second objective is to investigate the effect of gravity on sensor attachment by comparing simulations for the structure at $\alpha = 0$ and $90°$ (Fig. 4.6b) against those obtained experimentally. The comparison also provides a basis for validating (4.2) that relates the displacement w_s (for attaching a sensor) to the input displacement u_1.

(3) The third objective is to examine the effectiveness of the proposed strategy for crossing a corner. Of particular interest is to determine the required input displacement u_0 for a desired rotation angle θ as shown in Fig. 4.8.

For quantitative comparison, experimental results of the sensor attachment and corner negotiation processes were computed from images filmed by a camcorder (Sony HDR-SR11).

A.   *Validation of the beam model*

Figure 4.20a shows the experimental setup to examine the validity of the beam model, where the spring-steel laminate on one of two housing structures (Fig. 4.18b) was clamped as a cantilever, and thus has Type 1 constraints (Table 3.1). The remaining U-shaped portion (non-shaded in Fig. 4.18c) in the spring-steel laminate serves as a load at the end of the compliant beam (that has a non-uniform shape and thus non-uniform distributed weight). As the mass center of this U-shaped portion is located at 10.1 mm from the free end of the beam (Fig. 4.18c), the weight of this U-shaped portion also contributes to a lateral force F_U and a moment M_U in addition to the external payload m_p at the free end of the beam. As a result, the values of F_1, F_3 and M_2 in the boundary conditions are given by

$$F_1 = 0, \; F_3 = F_U + m_p g, \; M_2 = M_U \tag{4.16}$$

In this experiment, a strain gauge (with negligible weight as compared to the beam) was attached on the upper surface at the middle of the beam. To provide an alternative basis for comparisons, a numerical model was built in Abaqus using 6319 shell elements (S4R type). In FE analysis, only one-half of the beam is simulated because of symmetry, and the external load is applied at one coupling element so that F_U is uniformly distributed over the cross section at the beam tip. All computations were performed on a computer with a 2.99 GHz CPU and 4.00 GB memory; the FEA took about 365 s while the beam model (3-segment MSM) requires only 95 s. The results are given in Fig. 4.21, which compares the results of the two beam models are uniform width of 20.32 mm and non-uniform shape (that accounts for the geometry of the sensor holder), against those of FEA and experiment.

The results are discussed as follows:

(1) Fig. 4.21a shows that the FEA-computed beam-shapes and the uniform/non-uniform beam models closely agree with each other for two different loadings; external payload $m_p = 0$ and 50 g exerted at the beam tip.

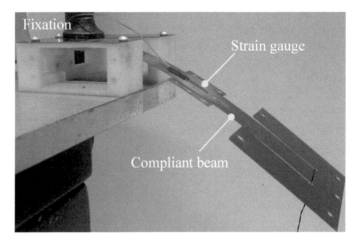

(a) Experiment setup

(b) Finite element analysis

Fig. 4.20 Validation of the beam model

(2) Figure 4.21b shows that the strain ε_{11} increases monotonically with the pay-load. The beam model agrees well with the experimental measurements. Some discrepancies at large payloads are observed in FEA possibly due to the following local effects:

  a. Because of FE meshes, the node at which strain information is extracted does not locate exactly at the middle of the beam.
  b. Besides, the FEA model can capture the local stress concentration while the strain gauge is actually measuring the average strain over its area, and the

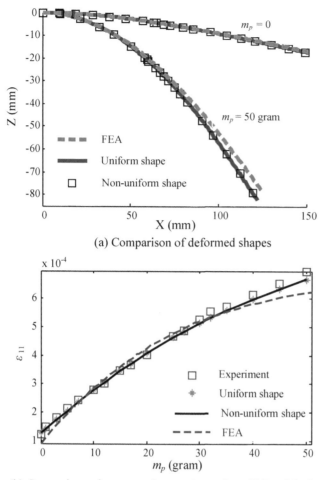

(a) Comparison of deformed shapes

(b) Comparison of upper-surface strains at the middle of the beam

Fig. 4.21 Model validation with FEA and experiment

stress concentration is not accounted in this beam model. When comparing this local information, the beam model matches with experiments but some discrepancy exists in the FEA.

It is noted that the ten-hole area takes up to 8% of that of the sensor holder, which was compensated for by a function characterizing the change in beam widths; thus the results from the two beam geometries, uniform and non-uniform shapes, do not differ significantly in this specific application.

B. *Effect of gravity on sensor attachment*

In this experiment, the sensor was attached on the plane by moving both axles towards each other to prevent slippage as shown in Fig. 4.22a–c. For comparing against analytical simulations where sensor attachments were modeled as a process of moving the front axle towards the fixed rear axle, the net displacement u_1 was obtained by measuring the distance change between the front and rear wheel centers from captured images. Figure 4.22d is a zoom-in comparison of Fig. 4.6b showing good agreements between analyses and experiment results for $\alpha = 0$, 45° and 90°.

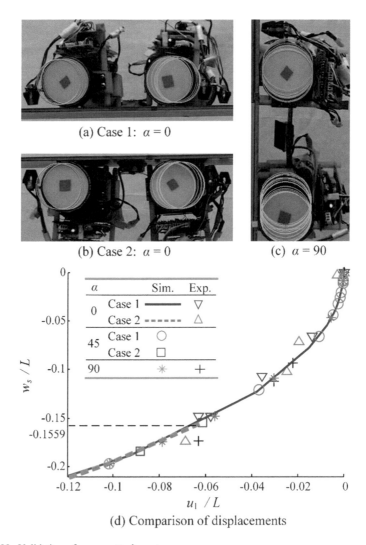

(a) Case 1: $\alpha = 0$

(b) Case 2: $\alpha = 0$ (c) $\alpha = 90$

(d) Comparison of displacements

Fig. 4.22 Validation of sensor attachment

The results are discussed as follows:

(1) It is worth noting that the deviation in Case 2 for $\alpha = 0$ was a result of the onset of buckling. Once the critical force is overcome, w_s /L jumps from zero to -0.1559. This non-linear dynamic is essentially unstable. Thus, in Case 2, the required input displacement u_1 for $w_s/L > -0.1559$ is of the same value ($u_1/L = -0.06$) as that when buckling starts.

(2) However, all the intermediate experiment data follows the continuous curve given by (4.2) which is independent of the slope angle α, therefore the relation between u_1 and w_s obtained from the static analysis is also valid for the dynamic process of Case 2.

(3) This also justifies for the conclusion obtained from Fig. 4.6 to control the compliant beam deformation by manipulating the input displacement u_1 rather than the input force F_1.

C. *Validation of the corner negotiation*

Figure 4.23a–c shows the three steps in negotiating a convex right corner by pushing the front axle, both axles moving together and finally pulling the rear axle. Following the earlier analysis, the rotation angle θ of the front axle is obtained by the orientation of the line connecting the front wheel center and the corner point, while the displacement u_0 of the rear axle is determined by the rear wheel center.
Observations are discussed as follows:

(1) Although the relation between the applied force F_1 and the desired rotation angle θ is nonlinear depending on the gravity direction, a highly linear relation $u_0 /L = 0.0051 \theta$ exists between u_0 and θ regardless of the gravity direction in the simulation as shown in Fig. 4.23d. Experiment results also confirm with this linear relation.

   a. It is noted that errors may come from the required torque that is calculated from the assembly mass and the distance from the corner to the mass center.

   b. Another source of error can be the image processing of the video frames when detecting the front and rear axle locations by wheel centers and determining the corner point by manually picking one pixel. Since the steel structure and the camcorder are fixed throughout the experiment, this corner point A is fixed in all the images while small vibrations can exist in the steel structure because of the FMN dynamics.

(2) It can also be seen that both the pushing and pulling process follow the same curve in experiment, implying that the aforementioned analysis for the pushing process (Step 1) can be applied throughout the corner negotiation.

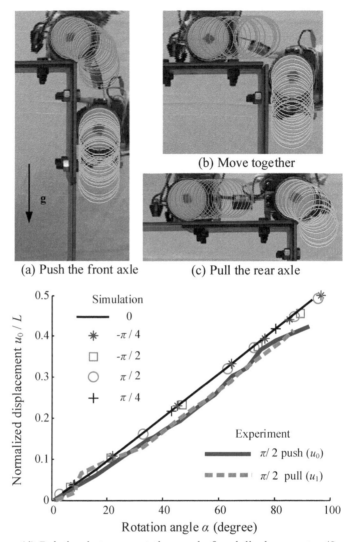

(a) Push the front axle   (c) Pull the rear axle

(b) Move together

(d) Relation between rotation angle θ and displacement u_0/L

Fig. 4.23 Convex right corner negotiation

4.3.2 Second Prototype of FMN

A modified FMN prototype is developed with a camera on the front axle as shown in Fig. 4.24. Two neodymium $90°$ arc magnets, which are radially magnetized in the opposite directions, are fixed with the frame body through the guards (radius is 30 mm), hence they do not rotate with the wheels. Each of the hollow wheels (inner and outer radii are 31 and 32.5 mm, respectively) is independently driven by one

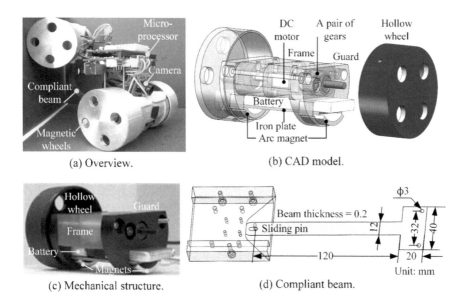

(a) Overview.

(b) CAD model.

(c) Mechanical structure.

(d) Compliant beam.

Fig. 4.24 The second prototype of FMN

DC motor. As a magnetic force decreases dramatically with distance, the gap between the magnets and the surface is designed to be about 3.5 mm. Also, an iron plate is added to increase the wheel attraction force by forming a closed-loop of the magnetic flux. Compared with the design in Fig. 4.18a that 18 magnets are attached around each wheel, this wheel configuration is featured with only one fixed magnet and the overall weight of one axle is measured as about 0.4 kg, which is mainly contributed by the motors, batteries and magnets as the main parts of the FMN are made of Delrin. So a robot designed with the fixed magnet configuration is anticipated to be lighter than those using rotating magnets in the traditional configuration.

Besides, this modified FMN prototype is also featured with the front axle yawing as shown in Fig. 4.15. To enable this DOF, the compliant beam is attached with the front axle via an on-off pin-joint. As shown in Fig. 4.24d, this pin joint is coupled with a linear slot, such that different boundary conditions are achievable based on the location of the pin axis (out of the paper) along the linear slot and the environment constraints. When the pin is located at the free location, there is a gap between the front edge of the beam and back of the front assembly allowing free rotation between them like a regular pin joint. As the pin axis is at the clamped location, the front edge of the beam is pushed against the back of the front axle, rendering a locking state that is equivalent to the fixed-end boundary condition. Besides, an accelerometer is fixed at the middle on the beam.

The objectives of the experiment are as follows:

(1) The first objective is to validate the proposed obstacle avoidance strategy for convex corner negotiation, where the pushing angle varies from $0°$ to $60°$.

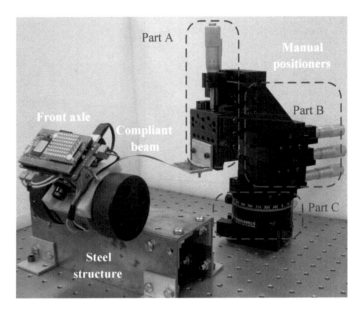

Fig. 4.25 Experimental setup

(2) The second is to validate the theoretical model for corner negotiation based on a compliant beam by comparing simulation result against experiment.

(3) The third is to determine the rear axle displacement u_0 for a desired front-axle rotation angle θ to implement the displacement control.

Figure 4.25 shows the experimental setup for the front axle to overcome a right corner on a steel structure. To accurately maintain the pushing angle ψ and measure the rear axle displacement u_0, the rear axle is replaced by a set of manual positioners. The translation stages in Part A are used to adjust the height of the compliant beam to obtain a horizontal initial state, while those in Part B measure the pushing displacement u_0 from 0 to 75 mm. The rotation stage in Part C is employed to manipulate ψ, thus can change the direction of the complaint beam relative to the front axle.

Snapshots of the front axle wheel are captured by a digital camera for each value of u_0 as shown in Fig. 4.26a, and the wheel center is calculated by image processing techniques. Then, the rotation angle θ of the front axle is obtained by the orientation of the line connecting the wheel center and the corner point. Since the simulation results for different ψ are very close to each other, average of the simulation result is compared against the cases of ψ increased from $0°$ to $60°$ with increment of $15°$ in Fig. 4.26b. It is shown that simulation closely matches with the experiment results, although deviations exist for $\psi = 0°$ and $30°$. It is noted that errors may come from calculation of the required torque that involves determination of the assembly mass center. Another error source would be the image processing

(a) Detection of front axle rotation.

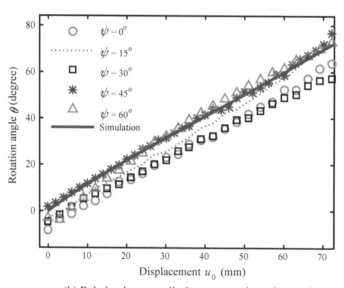

(b) Relation between displacement and rotation angle

Fig. 4.26 Experimental validation for relation between displacement and rotation angle

when the corner point is determined by manually picking one pixel, which may give rise to a nonzero initial value of θ. Besides, it is obvious that the rotation angle θ is linear with the rear axle displacement u_0 for different pushing angle ψ, which potentially facilitate the control implementation for corner negotiation.

4.4 Structural Health Monitoring

The application of the developed flexible robot is presented with structural health monitoring (SHM) and dynamic testing of large civil structures (such as ferromagnetic bridges) [2]. Current bridge inspections (relying on visual identification of damages on structure surfaces) are laborious and costly, and limited to once every two years; damages located below the surface often remain elusive to the inspectors. In order to reduce these costs, the mobile sensing node should be able to perform two functions; negotiating obstacles within a limited space on structures being inspected and attaching/detaching an accelerometer to collect data for vibration analysis. Thus, the mechanical structure of a mobile sensing node has to be flexible enough to successfully perform all these functions. Unlike other field robots designed solely on rigid links, compliant links offer more flexibility in maneuvering various poses for the robot, thus it is more adaptive to complex terrains. Moreover, by replacing revolute joints with flexible beams, it also reduces friction between components. When a mobile sensing node is incorporated with a compliant mechanism, it is called a flexure-based-mechatronic (Flexonic) Mobile Node (FMN). Application of the FMN to SHM is illustrated with two examples, one laboratory test on a steel frame structure and another field testing on a pedestrian bridge.

4.4.1 Steel Frame Structure

In [3], a modal analysis of a steel frame structure was conducted with data collected from four mobile sensing nodes, where sensors were not in contact with the measuring surface. The modal analysis in [3] was limited due to the dynamics of the mobile sensing node which essentially behaves as a low-pass filter. The interest here is to investigate the effect of sensor attachment on structural frequency identification using impulse response studies. For this, vertical vibration data were collected by an accelerometer. As compared in Fig. 4.27, the FMN firmly presses the accelerometer against the measured surface by the compliant beam, while the

(a) FMN   (b) Single axle [151]

Fig. 4.27 Comparison of flexible and rigid design configurations [3]

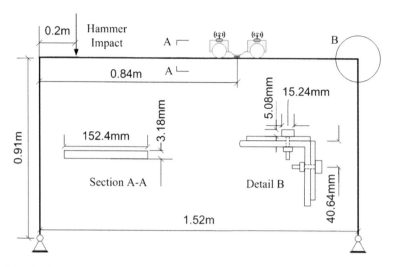

Fig. 4.28 Steel frame structure

Table 4.5 Steel frame material properties and robot dimensions

Material properties	Steel	Robot dimensions	
Elastic modulus (GPa)	210	Length (cm)	20
Shear modulus (GPa)	82	Width (cm)	14.7
Poisson ratio	0.28	Height (cm)	7.6
Density (kg/m³)	7700	Weight (kg)	1
Sampling frequency = 500 Hz			

accelerometer underneath the 3-wheel magnetic mobile node [3] is not in contact with the surface. As a basis for comparison, the fast Fourier transform results obtained from both measurements are compared against those predicted by FEA.

Figure 4.28 shows a 2D laboratory steel portal frame structure (consisting of a beam and two column members) constructed for structural modal analyses. The beam is connected to the columns by bolted angle plates and by hinge-connections at the column bases. The dimensions for the frame structure are shown in Fig. 4.28 along with material properties listed in Table 4.5. The two mobile robots are placed at the same position on the beam where vertical vibration data were collected after a hammer impact at a specified position. A sampling frequency of 500 Hz is used for the data collection. The results comparing the vertical vibration data (in the frequency domain) collected from the two robots are given in Fig. 4.29 and Table 4.6.

Some observations can be made from the results:

(1) The dynamics of both magnetic cars has little influence on the vibration measurements in the lower-frequency range (<50 Hz), and thus the results are closely matched with FEA results.

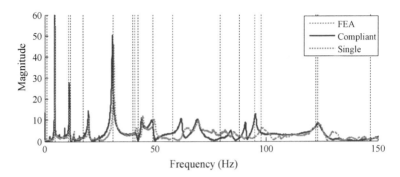

Fig. 4.29 FFT of vertical vibration in the steel frame

Table 4.6 Comparison of frequencies

FEA (Hz)	FMN (Hz)	Single axle (Hz)
1.009		
4.626	4.5	4.7
10.757		
11.642	11.2	11.2
17.573	19.9	20.1
30.970	30.8	31.3
39.946		
40.679	43.8	44.3
42.247		
48.816	48.3	49.5
57.758	*61.8*	
79.232		
87.724	*90.5*	
94.619	95.1	98.2
97.680		
122.150	123.3	124.2
123.130		
146.640		

(2) For this experiment configuration, the first vibration mode (horizontal) is not excited, so the lowest modal frequency is not identified. Also, since only one measuring point is considered in the experiment, some of the modal frequencies obtained from the FEA are not detected. Clearly, if this measuring point is at the zero-vibration positions of certain mode shapes, the corresponding frequencies for these mode shapes cannot be captured at this point suggesting that multiple measuring points are necessary in practice.

(3) For frequencies larger than 50 Hz, relatively sharp peaks can still be identified by the FMN because the accelerometer is firmly pressed against the steel frame structure eliminating the car dynamic effects on the measurements.

(4) As shown in Table 4.6, vibration frequencies denoted in italics were captured by the FMN but not the single-axle robot, because the accelerometer on the FMN is in direct contact with the measured surface while the sigle-axle structure acts like a filter to the acceleration signals.

4.4.2   Space Frame Bridge

This section investigates the field performance of the FMNs with a space frame pedestrian bridge on Georgia Tech campus. Multiple FMNs are wirelessly commanded to navigate to different sections of the steel bridge, for measuring structural vibrations at a high spatial resolution. Using a small number of FMNs, detailed modal characteristics of the bridge are identified.

A. *Field testing setup*

The pedestrian steel bridge testbed (Fig. 4.30) is located on Georgia Tech campus, connecting the Manufacturing Research Center (MARC) with the Manufacturing Related Disciplines Complex (MRDC). The bridge consists of eleven chord units. Diagonal tension bars are deployed in two vertical side planes and the top horizontal planes, and each floor unit contains a diagonal bracing tube. Hinge connections are designed at the supports on the MRDC side, and roller connections at the MARC side. Key dimensions of the bridge are listed in Table 4.7.

In the field testing, a set of instrumentation was conducted entirely with static wireless sensors for comparison. Static sensors were installed at the measurement locations on the top plane of the bridge frame (Fig. 4.31a). Modal analysis results using the static sensor data serve as a baseline for the FMN data. The Silicon

Fig. 4.30 Picture of the space frame bridge on Georgia Tech campus

Table 4.7 Dimensions of the steel bridge

Dimension		Value
Length		11 × 2.74 m = 30.2 m (99 ft)
Width		2.13 m (7 ft)
Height		2.74 m (9 ft)
Concrete floor slab thickness		0.139 m (5.5 in.)
Cross section and thickness of square tubes	Top-plane longitudinal	0.152 m × 0.152 m × 0.0080 m (6 in × 6 in × 5/16 in.)
	Bottom-plane longitudinal	0.152 m × 0.152 m × 0.0095 m (6 in × 6 in × 3/8 in.)
	Others	0.152 m × 0.152 m × 0.0064 m (6 in × 6 in × 1/4 in.)

Designs 2260-010 accelerometers were used in the static sensor instrumentation for measuring vertical vibrations. Four FMNs were deployed for navigating on the top plane of the frame. It was first verified that each FMN can travel through the bridge span of 30.2 m (99 ft) in about 5 min, without stop. Onboard lithium-ion batteries can sustain the FMN operation for about 4 h. A total of five measurement configurations were adopted by the FMNs. As shown in Fig. 4.31b, each configuration consists of four measurement locations. Locations at south side of the frame are marked with letter 'S', and locations at north side are marked with letter 'N'. The measurement configurations for the FMNs did not contain locations 4S and 4 N, where static wireless sensing nodes were mounted as reference nodes for assembling the mode shapes of the entire bridge. Wirelessly controlled by a laptop server located on the floor level at one side of the bridge Fig. 4.31c, the FMNs started from the inclined members at one side of the bridge (Fig. 4.32a), and then moved to the 1st measurement configuration (Fig. 4.32b). After finishing the measurement at the 1st configuration, the FMNs moved to the 2nd configuration, and so on, until they finished measurements at the 5th configuration.

At every measurement configuration, each FMN attached an accelerometer onto the structural surface, and measured structural vibrations along the vertical direction (Fig. 4.31c). The accelerometer used in this study is a single-axis accelerometer (Silicon Designs 2260-010) with a frequency bandwidth of 0–300 Hz. The measurement range is ±2 g, and the sensitivity is 1 V/g, where 'g' is the gravitational acceleration. For the wireless data transmission from the FMNs to the server, a simple star topology network was adopted. Acceleration data were temporarily stored onboard by each FMN, and then sequentially collected by the server. Detailed information about the wireless network operation can be found in [4].

B. *Field testing results*

Hammer impact tests with the FMNs were first conducted. Individual hammer impact was applied at two locations on the floor, which were directly below locations 4S and 8N in Fig. 4.33a. After the four FMNs arrived at each

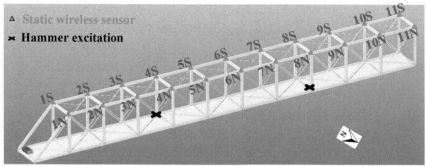

(a) Experimental setup for the testing with static wireless sensors.

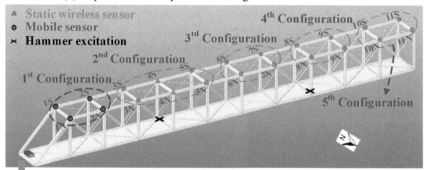

(b) 3D illustration of five measurement configurations for the FMNs.

(c) a laptop as the wireless server.   (d) a sensor is attached onto the surface.

Fig. 4.31 Experimental setup for the bridge testing

(a) FMNs start from the incline members.   (b) FMSNs arrive at the 1st sensing configuration.

Fig. 4.32 Pictures of four FMNs navigating on the space frame bridge

(a) a hammer impact being applied.

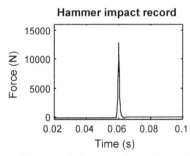

(b) example hammer impact record.

Fig. 4.33 Hammer impact test

configuration, hammer impact was first applied at the floor below 4S for data collection, and then another impact was applied below 8N. Figure 4.33a shows the picture of a hammer impact being applied with a 3-lb hammer manufactured by PCB Piezotronics. The impact head allows for different tips to be affixed to the end, for varying the impact frequency range. A soft plastic tip was used in this study, for generating flat impact spectra up to a few hundred Hertz. The impact force was recorded by a cabled DAQ system (National Instruments 9235) (Fig. 4.33b).

During hammer impact test, the amplification gain of the signal-conditioning module in the FMNs was set to ×20 for acceleration measurement. The sampling rate was set to 1000 Hz. Figure 4.34a presents example acceleration time histories recorded at locations 5S and 9N, as well as the corresponding frequency response function (FRF) plots when the hammer impact was applied on the floor below location 4S. Figure 4.34b shows some example acceleration time histories and corresponding FRF plots, when the impact was applied below location 8N. During the ambient vibration test, 10 min of continuous acceleration data were collected for each mobile measurement configuration. The amplification gain of the signal conditioning module was set to ×200 during ambient vibration test, and the sampling rate was set to 100 Hz. Figure 4.34c presents example ambient vibration time histories recorded at locations 5S and 9N, as well as the corresponding power spectral density (PSD) plots. The natural frequencies extracted from the hammer impact test and ambient vibration data are summarized in Table 4.8. The frequency differences extracted from the FMN data and static sensor data are very small.

4.5 Summary

The design concept of an FMN robot has been presented, where a flexible beam is incorporated for corner negotiation and sensor attachment. Its functionalities have been numerically analyzed in simulations with the beam models from Chap. 3 and experimentally validated on two FMN prototypes of different magnetic wheel

Fig. 4.34 Example vibration
records and corresponding
FRF/PSD plots

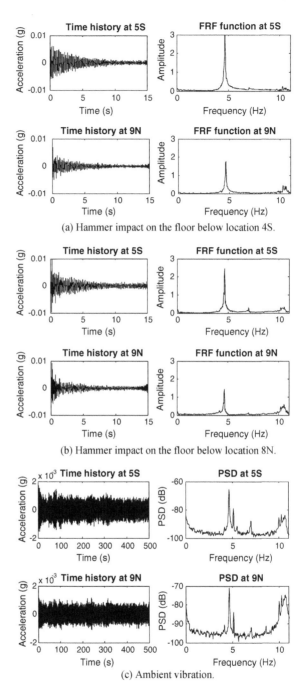

(a) Hammer impact on the floor below location 4S.

(b) Hammer impact on the floor below location 8N.

(c) Ambient vibration.

Table 4.8 Comparison of modal characteristics extracted from FMN data and static sensor data

Mode No.	Natural frequencies (Hz)		
	Mobile data (hammer)	Mobile data (ambient)	Static data (hammer)
1	4.63	4.67	4.64
2	6.97	6.92	6.93
3	10.53	10.28	10.51

configurations. Finally, the application of FMN is illustrated with structural health monitoring.

References

1. J.M. Gere, S.P. Timoshenko, *Mechanics of Materials*, 4th edn. (PWS, Boston, 1997)
2. K.-M. Lee, Y. Wang, D. Zhu, J. Guo, X. Yi, Flexure-based mechatronic mobile sensors for structure damage detection, presented at the *7th International Workshop on Structural Health Monitoring*, Stanford CA, USA (2009)
3. S.H. Foong, K.M. Lee, Magnetic field-based multi-DOF orientation sensor for PM-based spherical actuators, in *Proceedings of IEEE/ASME International Conference on Advanced Intelligent Mechatronics (AIM)*, Singapore, vol. 1–3, pp. 481–486 (2009)
4. Y. Wang, J.P. Lynch, K.H. Law, A wireless structural health monitoring system with multithreaded sensing devices: design and validation. Struct. Infrastruct. Eng. **3**(2), 103–120 (2007)

Chapter 5
Intelligent Manufacturing

Machining complex thin-wall components (such as compressor disks and casings in aircraft engines) has been a challenging task because workpiece deformations and vibrations not only compromise the surface integrity but also induce residual stresses in the final products. Based on the annular plate model in Chap. 3, this chapter presents a physics-based method that accounts for the damping effects and external loads for reconstructing the dynamic displacement and strain fields of a thin-wall workpiece in real-time with non-contact displacement measurements during machining. In order to establish criteria for designing non-contact sensors to monitor workpiece vibration, this chapter also presents plate dynamic analysis along with experimentally identified damping ratios for an annular workpiece under constraints emulating those of a duplex turning machine. Given that plate dynamic behaviors can be characterized by superposition of mode shapes, the time-varying displacement and strain fields are reconstructed with modal coefficients that are updated in real time using in situ measurements.

5.1 Dynamic Analysis

An application illustrating the calculation of the natural frequencies and mode shapes of the thin-wall plate dynamic model is illustrated in Fig. 5.1a, b which emulate a two-sided lathe turning center of a thin-wall compressor disk constrained by two fixture design configurations (DCs):

DC1 illustrates a lathe machining center where a thin-wall compressor disk is machined by duplex turning. The workpiece is clamped at the outer and inner edges on the rotating fixture driven by a motor through a belt-drive mechanism; thus,

$$\text{BCs at } R = \gamma_b \text{ and } 1 \qquad (3.33a, b)$$

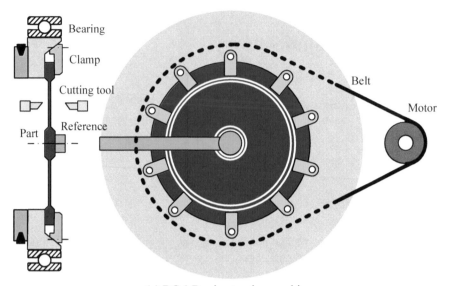

(a) DC 1 Duplex turning machine.

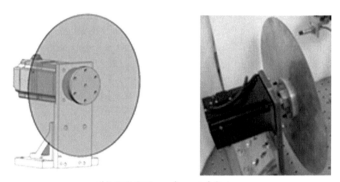

(b) DC 2 Experimental Setup.

Fig. 5.1 Fixation of a thin annular workpiece

DC2 is an experimental test-bed where the inner edge of the workpiece is fixed on the shaft of a direct-drive motor, and the outer edge is free:

$$\text{BC at } R = \gamma_b \qquad\qquad\qquad (3.33a, b)$$

$$\text{BC at } R = 1 \qquad\qquad\qquad (3.33c, d)$$

Although DC2 is a simplified version of DC1, its boundary conditions are more complicated for the computation.

Table 5.1 Plate specifications in simulation

	Aluminum	TC4	Inconel 718
Density, ρ (kg/m^3)	2700	4430	8190
Elastic modulus, E (GPa)	70	113.8	200
Poisson ratio, υ	0.35	0.342	0.294
Feature speed, c_w (m/s)	1566.7	1557.0	1492.3
Outer radius, a (mm)	150		
Inner radius, b (mm)	40		
Thickness, h (mm)	1, 2, 3, 4		
Spindle speed, Ω (rpm)	0, 300, 600		
Normalized speed, $\bar{\Omega}$ (1×10^{-5})	1.4361 Ω/h	1.4451 Ω/h	1.5077 Ω/h
Normalized thickness, γ_h	0.0067 h where h = 1, 2, 3, 4 mm		

The effects of working conditions (including Ω and h) on the natural frequencies are investigated with the parametric values listed in Table 5.1. Simulation results are compared against FEA which serves as basis for numerical verification.

5.1.1 Parametric Effects on $|A(\omega_{nm})|$ (DC1)

The spindle speed Ω is an important operating parameter for controlling chatter vibration during machining where the thickness h decreases as cutting proceeds. Figure 5.2 plots $|A(\bar{\omega}_{nm})|$ for a given annular γ_b design under different operating conditions (Ω from 0 to 600 rpm, and h from 1 to 4 mm), where the local minimums representing the roots of (3.39) correspond to the normalized natural frequencies with prescribed calculation tolerance of 10^{-6}.

As shown in Fig. 5.2 for DC1 and DC2, respectively, the computed $|A(\bar{\omega}_{nm})|$ collapses into a single curve validating the physical significance of the normalization (3.25). Given the normalization (3.25f) and single normalized curve for each DC, it can be concluded that ω_{nm} decreases linearly with h as cutting proceeds. Because the constraint on the outer edge of DC2 is relaxed, DC2 embodies one more normalized natural frequency than DC1 within [0 100] for n =1 as seen in the comparison between Fig. 5.2a, b; and also the dominant natural frequency for DC2 is much lower than that of DC1.

With prescribed tolerance of 10^{-6}, the method presented here took 2.58 s (3 or less iterations for each mode) to obtain the first four modes in DC2 as compared to 2.6 s with Abaqus on the same computer (3.5 GHz CPU, 32 GB RAM).

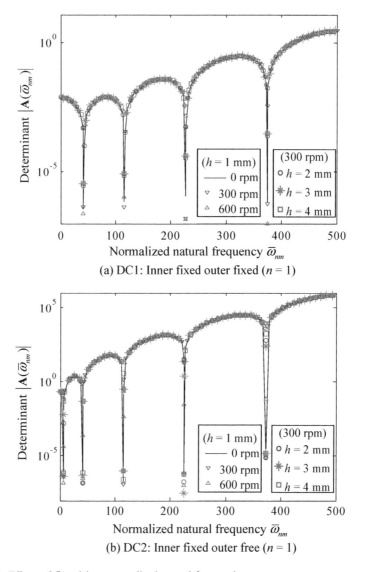

Fig. 5.2 Effects of Ω and h on normalized natural frequencies

5.1.2   *Illustrative Example (DC1)*

Simulation results numerically predict the normalized natural frequencies and mode shapes for DC1 for illustrating the model analysis are plotted in Fig. 5.3 together with the physical meanings of n and m. Some observations can be drawn from the above results:

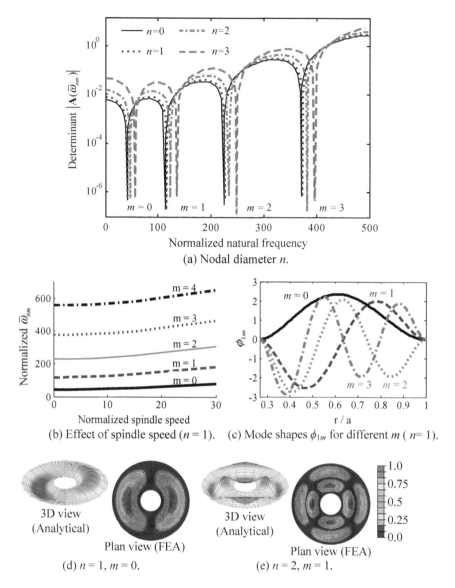

Fig. 5.3 Distribution of natural frequencies and mode shapes (DC1)

- Figure 5.4a compares $|\mathbf{A}(\omega_{nm})|$ for different n values. The distribution of the natural frequencies is discrete and fall into groups labeled by m from the smallest values. Within each group (same m), ω_{nm} increases with n monotonically.

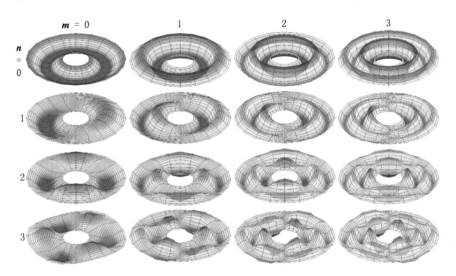

Fig. 5.4 Mode shapes of an annular plate subjected to DC1 constraint

- Figure 5.3b shows the normalized ω_{nm} increases with normalized spindle speed from 0 to 30 for $n = 1$, but does not change much under 15 confirming the results in Fig. 5.2.
- Figure 5.3c plots ϕ_{1m} for various values of m for r ranging from $R = \gamma_b$ to 1. The number of zeroes is equal to m excluding those at $R = \gamma_b$ and 1 prescribed by the BCs.
- The physical meanings of n diametric and m circular zero nodal displacements (excluding the inner and/or outer circles assigned by fixed BCs) are illustrated with analytically computed 3D plots of $[\phi_{nm}(r) \, e^{in\theta}]$ in Fig. 5.3d for $n = 1$ and $m = 0$ and Fig. 5.3e for $n = 2$ and $m = 1$, which are compared against the FEA simulated plan views. In other words, there is a diametric ($n = 1$) zero nodal displacements and no circular ($m = 0$) zero nodal displacement during vibration as seen in Fig. 5.3d. Similarly, $n = 2$ diametric and $m = 1$ circular zero nodal displacements can be seen in Fig. 5.3e. With the mode shape symmetry, the angle between the locations of maximum and zero vibration magnitudes can be obtained as

$$\theta = \left(k + \frac{1}{2}\right) \frac{180°}{n} \quad \text{where} \quad k = 0, 1, 2, \ldots \tag{5.1}$$

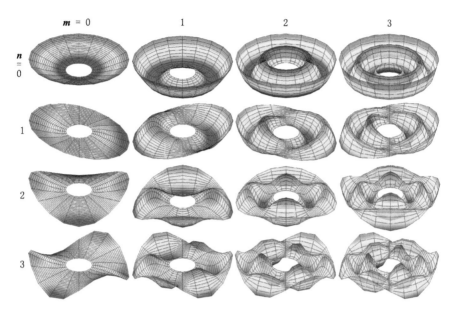

Fig. 5.5 Mode shapes of an annular plate subjected to DC2 constraint

5.1.3 Numerical Verification (DC1 and DC2)

The computed mode shapes of an annular plate subjected to DC1 and DC2 constraints are shown in Figs. 5.4 and 5.5. For each mode shapes, the corresponding normalized natural frequencies are also compared with FEA results in Tables 5.2 and 5.3, respectively; the percentage differences are within 4% for DC1 and 2% for DC2, respectively, for the 16 modes of n, $m = 0, 1, 2, 3$.

5.2 Parameter Identification and Sensing Configuration

To validate the dynamic model and related analysis, impulse response experiments were conducted on the DC2 test-bed (Fig. 5.1b) where the thin-wall annular plate (Table 5.1) was clamped at the inner edge on the shaft of a servo motor (Yaskawa SGMJV-08ADE6S) as shown in Fig. 5.6. A pair of eddy-current sensors (CWY-DO-20XLT08-M10) with specifications given in Table 5.4 was employed to measure the vibration of the thin plate, which was intrigued by an impulse with an impact hammer or a step change from an initial deformation.

The objectives of the three experiments are as follows:

(1) **Measure of damping ratios**: For different modes, there are corresponding modal damping ratios, which have to be obtained in experiment. The setup is

Table 5.2 Comparison of ω_{nm} against FEA (DC1), units in Hz

(n, m)	This book	FEA	% error
(0, 0)	457.4	459.5	0.34
(0, 1)	1265.0	1280.1	1.1
(0, 2)	2484.5	2541.2	2.2
(0, 3)	4110.9	4268.6	3.6
(1, 0)	472.5	474.6	0.32
(1, 1)	1289.0	1303.8	1.01
(1, 2)	2512.8	2567.8	2.1
(1, 3)	4141.8	4296.6	3.6
(2, 0)	526.2	528.4	0.20
(2, 1)	1364.8	1380.3	0.83
(2, 2)	2599.6	2657.6	1.9
(2, 3)	4235.8	4395.4	3.1
(3, 0)	633.8	636.49	0.27
(3, 1)	1500.7	1517.2	0.91
(3, 2)	2750.5	2808.9	2.0
(3, 3)	4396.3	4566.0	3.4

Table 5.3 Comparison of ω_{nm} against FEA (DC2), units in Hz

(n, m)	This book	FEA	% error
(0, 0)	68.30	68.08	0.33
(0, 1)	430.67	431.82	0.27
(0, 2)	1246.61	1257.8	0.89
(0, 3)	2465.38	2513.3	1.9
(1, 0)	65.82	65.53	0.44
(1, 1)	453.31	454.4	0.24
(1, 2)	1274.13	1284.9	0.84
(1, 3)	2496.25	2543.7	1.8
(2, 0)	80.38	80	0.48
(2, 1)	525.65	526.36	0.14
(2, 2)	1359.73	1368.9	0.67
(2, 3)	2590.62	2633.4	1.6
(3, 0)	140.63	140.3	0.23
(3, 1)	654.98	656.32	0.20
(3, 2)	1510.17	1521.7	0.76
(3, 3)	2752.99	2801.5	1.7

shown in Fig. 5.6a that nodal vibration displacement was measured by an eddy-current sensor without fluids, based on which damped frequencies and modal damping ratios are obtained.

(2) **Robustness of an eddy-current sensor**: Tests of sensor robustness were carried out with various fluids filling the gap between the sensor and plate surface

Fig. 5.6 Experimental
vibration test setup using
eddy-current sensors

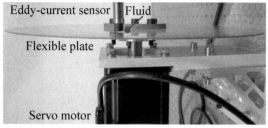

(a) Test using one eddy-current sensor.

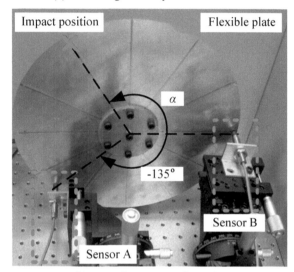

(b) Test of sensor configuration.

Table 5.4 Specifications of sensors

Parameters		Performance	
Eddy-current Sensor (CWY-DO-20XLT08-M10)			
Diameter (mm)	8	Response (kHz)	10
Standoff (mm)	0.5	Range (mm)	2
Input (Vdc)	-24	Resolution (μm)	0.1
Output (Vdc)	-18 to -2	Linearity ($\pm$ % FS)	1
		Temp. stability (% FSR/°C)	0.04
Laser Displacement Sensor (Keyence LK-H025)			
Ref. distance (mm)	20	Sampling rate (kHz)	2
Spot diameter (μm)	25 × 1400	Range (mm)	$\pm$ 3
Wavelength (nm)	655	Repeatability (μm)	0.02
Output (mW)	4.8	Linearity ($\pm$ % FS)	0.02
		Temp. stability (% FSR/°C)	0.01
Strain Gauge (BFH350-1AA-S)			
Gauge pattern	uniaxial	Gauge resistance (Omega)	350
Base diameter (mm)	3.6 × 3.1	Gauge factor (mV/V)	2 $\pm$ 1%
Gauge length (mm)	1.0 × 2.0	Mechanical hysteresis (μm/m)	1.2
		Range	0.01

(Fig. 5.6a) to emulate harsh manufacturing conditions. The focus is to see how manufacturing conditions may affect conclusions obtained from modal analysis without fluids in Sect. 5.1.

(3) **Sensor configuration**: Applications of modal analysis for designing sensor configurations and understanding the effects of sensor locations on measurements are investigated. As shown in Fig. 5.6b, two eddy-current sensors are employed to measure the plate vibration; Sensor A is fixed at 135° clockwise from the referenced horizontal position where Sensor B is mounted. The plate vibration is activated by an impact at an angle α from the reference.

5.2.1 Modal Damping Ratios

Figure 5.7 shows the impulse response signal captured by an eddy-current sensor, and the frequency spectrum obtained by taking fast Fourier transform (FFT) of the measured data. According to Fig. 5.7a, the natural frequencies do not change with slow rotational speeds (from 0 to less than 1000 rpm); thus, the plate was not rotated in the following experiments. From peak values in the frequency spectrum shown in Fig. 5.7b, experimental results (damped frequencies) are obtained and organized in an ascending order (Table 5.5) corresponding to the analysis results (natural frequencies) obtained in Sect. 5.1.

Employing bandpass filters, each vibration mode can be isolated and the modal displacements are approximated by logarithmic curves defined by

$$\log w_{nm} = -\mu_{nm}\omega_{nm}t + \log(\max|w_{nm}|)$$

where $\max|w_{nm}|$ is the maximum magnitude of w_{nm}. The modal damping ratio μ_{nm} can then be obtained with linear regression methods. The displacement of mode (2, 1) and its approximated envelop is illustrated in Fig. 5.7c as an example. The results are shown in Table 5.5 that μ_{nm} decreases with increasing n, meaning that damping ratios are smaller for higher-order modes, which matches with common observations in engineering.

5.2.2 Step Response

To predict the effect of a step change in the normal force acting on the thin-wall workpiece from a machine tool on its vibration, experiments were conducted on the setup shown in Fig. 5.6; the results provide a basis for validating the modal damping identification method. The thin plate was given an initial deflection on the edge and released to vibrate freely. The results are given in Fig. 5.8.

Analytically, the step response at the sensing point $(r, \theta) = (a, 0)$ can be obtained by modifying the solution (3.24) to incorporate the modal damping in Table 5.5:

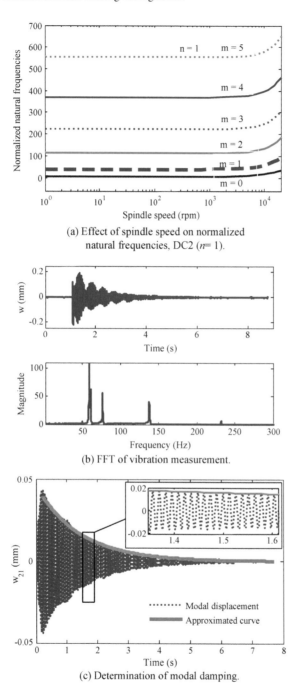

(a) Effect of spindle speed on normalized
natural frequencies, DC2 (n= 1).

(b) FFT of vibration measurement.

(c) Determination of modal damping.

Fig. 5.7 Vibration test of impulse response (DC2)

Table 5.5 Comparison of natural and damped frequencies

(n, m)	Analysis (Hz)	Experiment (Hz)	Damping ratio
(1,0)	65.82	58.07	0.0031
(0,0)	68.30	61.39	0.0034
(2,0)	80.38	77.23	0.0017
(3,0)	140.63	137.44	0.0011
(4,0)	238.26	231.07	0.0009

Fig. 5.8 Transient response with analysis and experiment

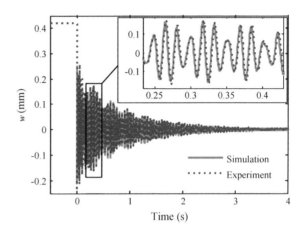

Table 5.6 Values of coefficients

Mode	(1,0)	(0,0)	(2,0)	(3,0)	(4,0)
a_{n1}	0.1137	0.0335	0.0486	0.0065	0.0027
b_{n1}	0.0853	0.0251	0.0364	0.0049	0.0020

$$w(t, a, 0) \simeq \sum_{n=0}^{4} e^{-\mu_{n1}\omega_{n1}t}[a_{n1}\cos(\omega_{n1}t) + b_{n1}\sin(\omega_{n1}t)] \qquad (5.2)$$

where a_{n1} and b_{n1} are weight coefficients and have accounted for the value of $\phi_{nm}(r)e^{in\theta}$ at $(r, \theta) = (a, 0)$. Numerical values of a_{n1} and b_{n1} are listed in Table 5.6. Figure 5.8 compares the simulation result of (5.2) against experiment data, where the close match indicates that (5.2) captures the plate dynamics and the method provides a competent candidate for real time sensing of workpiece vibration.

5.2.3 Robustness of Sensor Performance

Figure 5.9a compares the frequency spectrums obtained using an eddy-current sensor with various fluids against that obtained with air; for covering a broad range of media, cutting fluid, tap water (electric conductive) and distilled water (electric non-conductive) were used. For each type of fluids, ten tests were done and maximum deviations from the result of air are plotted in error bars as shown in Fig. 5.9b. The small deviations indicate that the eddy-current sensor has a stable performance under different media conditions and can be a potential candidate for harsh condition monitoring during machining. With these consistent results, it is reasonable to conclude that as long as the sensor specification is appropriate for the working conditions, modal analyses assuming no fluids between the eddy-current sensor and workpiece are valid under practical manufacturing conditions Actual measuring results (like frequencies and damping), however, can be affected by process conditions (such as fixation configuration).

Fig. 5.9 Robustness of an eddy-current sensor with various media

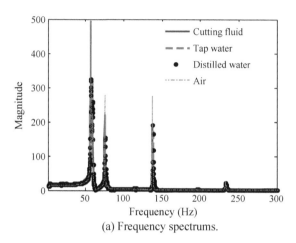

(a) Frequency spectrums.

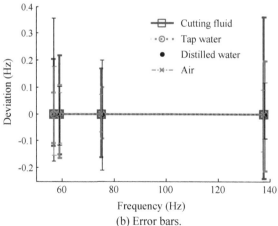

(b) Error bars.

5.2.4 Sensor Configuration Design

Theoretically, all vibration modes are activated as an impulse hits the plate. It is noted that whichever vibration modes are activated, the impact position vibrates with the maximum magnitude. For $\alpha = 42°$, the frequency spectrum in Fig. 5.10a shows that Sensor A captures all four lowest natural frequencies as obtained in Table 5.5, while Sensor B misses the 77.23 Hz predicting its magnitude similar to lower frequency noises. It can be seen that the third vibration mode (2, 0) corresponding to 77.23 Hz has two nodal diameters and zero nodal circle. Sensor A detects the location with the maximum vibration magnitude (in red color) while

Fig. 5.10 Stability of eddy-current sensing with various media

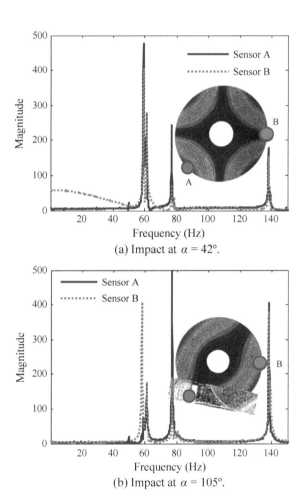

(a) Impact at $\alpha = 42°$.

(b) Impact at $\alpha = 105°$.

Sensor B measures the zero vibration zone (in blue color), so Sensor A can capture the third mode and Sensor B could not. For $\alpha = 105°$ (Fig. 5.10b), Sensor A locates at the zero vibration position (in blue color) of the (1, 0) mode, so it fails to capture this lowest frequency of 58.07 Hz; and Sensor B is able to detect all lowest natural frequencies.

These results suggest that the sensor placement should avoid zero vibration locations when configuring sensors for vibration deployment; in other words, optimal sensing results could be achieved by placing sensors at positions where maximum vibration magnitudes occur. With (5.1), theoretical results are $\theta = 45°$ and 90° for $\alpha = 42°$ and 105° with 6.7 and 16.7% errors respectively. This deviation may be due to manual manipulation of the impact hammer which results in error in the measured α, and the imperfection of the plate flatness which may distort the mode shapes.

5.3   Formulation of Field Reconstruction

Figure 5.11 shows two examples of circular thin-wall (thickness h) components modeled in cylindrical coordinates $[\mathbf{e}_r\ \mathbf{e}_\theta\ \mathbf{e}_z]$, where the referenced mid-surfaces are spanned by $\mathbf{e}_r$ and $\mathbf{e}_\theta$ axes, and $\mathbf{e}_z$ is aligned with the revolution axis. Figure 5.11a, b illustrate an annular plate model where the radial dimension of the mid-surface is given by $b \leq r \leq a$; and the location of a plate element is described in terms of (r, θ). For a cylindrical shell $(r = a)$ in Fig. 5.11c, d, its element is located by the coordinates (z, θ). The constraints can be imposed on either one or both boundaries of the components; the elements are subjected to plane strain states. As the thickness h which may be a non-uniform function of the element location is very small compared to its radius $(h \ll a)$, the thin-wall component can be represented by its mid-surface, and has the smallest stiffness in the normal direction of its mid-surface. Thus, the deformation of the component is dominant by the out-of-surface displacement $w(t, r, \theta)$ for the plate model or $w(t, z, \theta)$ for the shell model. The interest here is to reconstruct the continuous distributions of the out-of-plane displacement field and normal/shear strains by superimposing the corresponding mode shapes, where the time-varying coefficients are determined by a finite set of local discrete measurements. The following formulation assumes that the material property is linear elastic and homogeneous across the component; the shear deformations are neglected across the small thickness. The strain fields $\boldsymbol{\varepsilon} = [\varepsilon_{11}, \varepsilon_{22}, \varepsilon_{12}]^{\mathrm{T}}$ are given by

$$\boldsymbol{\varepsilon} = \mathbf{L}_w^\varepsilon w \qquad (5.3)$$

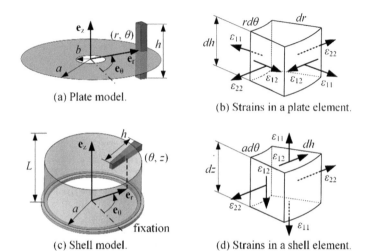

(a) Plate model.

(b) Strains in a plate element.

(c) Shell model.

(d) Strains in a shell element.

Fig. 5.11 Models for circular thin-wall components

where

$$
\mathbf{L}_w^\varepsilon =
\begin{cases}
-z\left[\dfrac{\partial^2}{\partial r^2} \quad \dfrac{\partial^2}{r^2\partial\theta^2}+\dfrac{\partial}{r\partial r} \quad \dfrac{2\partial^2}{r\partial r\partial\theta}-\dfrac{2\partial}{r^2\partial\theta}\right]^{\mathrm{T}} & \text{for plate} \\[2ex]
-r\left[\dfrac{\partial^2}{\partial z^2} \quad \dfrac{\partial^2}{a^2\partial\theta^2} \quad \dfrac{2\partial^2}{a\partial z\partial\theta}\right]^{\mathrm{T}}+\left[0 \quad \dfrac{1}{a} \quad 0\right]^{\mathrm{T}} & \text{for shell}
\end{cases}.
$$

While the presented method is formulated for an annular plate and a cylindrical shell, it can be extended to other coordinate frames following a similar procedure of variable separation. For generality, we denote the physical field as $P(t, \mathbf{s})$ in terms of the time t and location vector $\mathbf{s} = [s_1, s_2]^{\mathrm{T}}$ where s_1 and s_2 are two coordinate variables characterizing the mid-surface. In Fig. 5.11a, b or Fig. 5.11c, d, (s_1, s_2) represent the (r, θ) or (z, θ) coordinates of an element in the annular plate or cylindrical shell, respectively such that ε_{11} and ε_{22} are the normal strains along s_1 and s_2 whereas ε_{12} is the shear strain. Without loss of generality, the time-varying physical field P is expressed as a serial product of time and spatial components:

$$
P(t, \mathbf{s}) = \sum_{k=0}^{+\infty} \alpha_k(t)\Phi_k^p(\mathbf{s}) \tag{5.4}
$$

where, Φ_k^p is the kth mode-shape (corresponding to P) determined by the component inertia and stiffness as well as the boundary constraints; and α_k's are the modal coefficients accounting for the accumulative time-varying effects of the intrinsic damping, initial conditions and external inputs. The estimated quantity can be approximated by the modes of the lowest K orders:

$$\tilde{P}(t,\mathbf{s}) = \sum_{k=0}^{K} \alpha_k(t)\Phi_k^p(\mathbf{s}) \tag{5.5}$$

With measured P at N different locations $\mathbf{s}_j$, $j = 1, 2, \ldots, N$, α_k's can be obtained from (5.4) according to the least square method:

$$\boldsymbol{\alpha} = (\mathbf{S}^T\mathbf{S})^{-1}\mathbf{S}^T\tilde{\mathbf{P}} \tag{5.6}$$

where

$$\tilde{\mathbf{P}} = \left[\tilde{P}(\tau,\mathbf{s}_1) \cdots \tilde{P}(\tau,\mathbf{s}_N)\right]^T, \quad \boldsymbol{\alpha}(t) = [\alpha_1 \, \alpha_2 \ldots \alpha_K]^T,$$

and

$$\mathbf{S} = \begin{bmatrix} \Phi_1^P(\mathbf{s}_1) & \Phi_2^P(\mathbf{s}_1) & \cdots & \Phi_K^P(\mathbf{s}_1) \\ \Phi_1^P(\mathbf{s}_2) & \Phi_2^P(\mathbf{s}_2) & \cdots & \Phi_K^P(\mathbf{s}_2) \\ \vdots & \vdots & \ddots & \vdots \\ \Phi_1^P(\mathbf{s}_N) & \Phi_2^P(\mathbf{s}_N) & \cdots & \Phi_K^P(\mathbf{s}_N) \end{bmatrix}.$$

5.3.1   Field Reconstruction Algorithm

With the general field reconstruction and mode-shapes formulated above, the displacement and strain fields can be independently reconstructed using (5.4) where the corresponding coefficient $\boldsymbol{\alpha}$ is determined from (5.6) with corresponding measurements. However, given the displacement and strain fields share the same coefficient $\boldsymbol{\alpha}(t)$ as can be derived from (5.3), an indirect but simple yet effective approach is employed to determine $\boldsymbol{\alpha}$ from (5.6) only with measured displacement data. To define dimensionless-variable groups to account for effects of the non-constant thickness on the physical fields

$$\frac{e}{\varepsilon} = \frac{1}{h^2/a^2}, \frac{W}{w/h} = \frac{R}{r/a} = \frac{\Theta}{\theta} = \frac{Z}{z/L} = 1,$$

(5.3) is rewritten as (5.7) with the elements (r, θ, z, a) in $\mathbf{L}_w^\varepsilon$ replaced with $(R, \Theta, Z, 1)$ in $\mathbf{L}_W^e$:

$$\mathbf{e} = \mathbf{L}_W^e W \tag{5.7}$$

Given that (5.4) is valid for both displacement and strains, (5.7) indicates that the normalized strain mode-shapes $\mathbf{\Phi}^e = [\Phi_{11}, \Phi_{22}, \Phi_{12}]^T$ are related to the displacement mode-shape Φ^W via (5.8):

$$\mathbf{\Phi}^e = \mathbf{L}_W^e \Phi^W \tag{5.8}$$

Moreover, the modal coefficients $\alpha(t)$ for both displacement and strain fields are identical at each time instance, and $\mathbf{L}_W^e$ is independent of t.

In many applications, non-contact strain measurements are not as accessible as displacement sensing; thus, the indirect approach is employed to reconstruct the strain distributions with the coefficients determined from the displacement measurements using (5.6) and the procedure is detailed below:

1. Obtain Φ^W for a given configuration from a modal analysis.
2. Differentiate Φ^W to obtain $\mathbf{\Phi}^e$ with (5.8).
3. Measure w and calculate its normalized value W at the discrete locations $\mathbf{s}_j = \begin{bmatrix} s_1 & s_2 \end{bmatrix}_j^T$ where $\mathbf{s}_j = (R_j, \Theta_j)$ or (Z_j, Θ_j), and $j = 1, 2, \ldots, N$ across the flexible part surface.
4. Calculate α from (5.6) where P is specified as W.
5. Obtain the displacement and strain fields by substituting α into (5.5) with $P = W$ and $P = e$, respectively.
6. Finally, the dimensional quantities w or ε can be obtained from the normalized values.

In Steps 1 and 2 above, the mode-shapes are calculated offline and stored in a database so that the computation does not affect the efficiency of the online reconstruction. The noise due to the derivatives in $\mathbf{L}_W^e$ in (5.8) can be minimized within a prescribed tolerance using a numerical filter. Unlike commonly used dynamic analysis methods (such as FEA) where α is numerically solved from a large-scale system formulated by the governing differential equations with known inputs, the method introduced here captures the field dynamics with real-time measurements and computes α with simple linear algebraic operations; thus, it is practical and efficient for online applications.

5.3.2   Numerical Verification

The reconstruction method is numerically verified by comparing results with FEA. The annular plate (with a clamped inner-edge and a free outer-edge, $h = 1$ mm) is chosen as an illustrative example [1], where the parametric values are listed in Table 5.1; and an impulse response (experimentally captured by an eddy-current displacement sensor) and its frequency spectrum are available in Fig. 5.7b. It is suggested that the plate dynamics can be approximated by the superposition of the lowest three mode shapes for reconstructing the displacement and strain fields, which justifies the reduction in the number of modes in (5.5) for subsequent reconstructions. The strain and displacement mode shapes as well as the mode-shape matrix **S** of the thin-wall annular plate are numerically calculated using the shooting method [1]. In Table 5.7, the published (1st column) displacement mode-shapes can be used to compute the different strain mode-shapes (second to fourth columns) of the lowest orders using (5.8).

As a basis for verification, the displacement/strain fields of the annular plate are simulated using FEA. The plate is subjected to a normalized concentrated force f_z (=0.0045, equivalent to 10N for the Al6016 plate) at the free edge (150 mm, 0°), and then relieved to simulate a zero-damping free vibration due to a step change. The simulated shape of the plate is shown in Fig. 5.12a where the strains are found primarily in the sector area $-50° \leq \theta \leq 50°$ around the loading point. Using the FEA results as "simulated measurements", the modal coefficients (α_k where $k = 0, 1$ and 2) are estimated from (5.6) using 5 measurements at the cylindrical coordinates $r = 110$ mm and $\theta = 45°$, 315° and at $r = 140$ mm and $\theta = 0°$, 33°, 327°. The static and dynamic (displacement/strain) fields reconstructed from (5.5) are presented in Fig. 5.12c, d respectively.

The upper and lower rows in Fig. 5.12c are the static reconstructed fields and their errors relative to the FEA results respectively. The radial strain ε_{rr} (upper row) has its maximum at the fixed inner edge and is zero at the free edge. On the other hand, the tangential strain $\varepsilon_{\theta\theta}$ is zero at the fixed inner edge. Around the loading, $\varepsilon_{\theta\theta}$ is in tensile along two radii and compressive on its bottom surface ($z = -h/2$) which is opposite on the upper surface ($z = h/2$). Unlike the normal (radial ε_{rr} and tangential $\varepsilon_{\theta\theta}$) strains which are symmetric due to bending, the shear strain $\varepsilon_{r\theta}$ is

Table 5.7 Mode shapes

Mode	Displacement Φ^W	Strains Φ_{RR}	$\Phi_{\Theta\Theta}$	$\Phi_{R\Theta}$
(0, 0)				
(1, 0)				
(2, 0)				
(3, 0)				

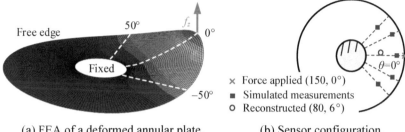

(a) FEA of a deformed annular plate.   (b) Sensor configuration.

× Force applied $(150, 0°)$
■ Simulated measurements
○ Reconstructed $(80, 6°)$

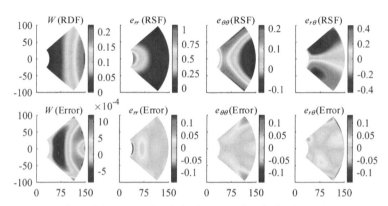

(c) Reconstruction of the normalized displacement/strain fields and error analysis.

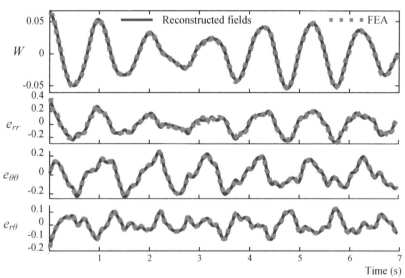

(d) Transient responses of the normalized nodal displacement/strains.

Fig. 5.12 Field reconstruction verified with FEA

antisymmetric about $\theta = 0°$ because of the plate twisting due to the applied force. The maximum error of the reconstructed strains (after multiplying the normalization factor h^2/a^2) is approximately 10^{-5} where the largest strain is about 10^{-4}. This 10% error (larger than the displacement reconstruction error of approximately 1%) is somewhat expected as the strains are inferred from the measured displacements.

In Fig. 5.12d, the reconstructed displacement/strains of the free vibration are compared with the FEA results. The comparisons verify that the proposed reconstruction method can track the time-varying displacement/strains closely when the plate is in free vibration. It is also observed that all the three strains vary with multiple modes like the displacement, validating the formulation of the strain mode-shapes and its field reconstruction application.

5.3.3 Numerical Evaluation of Reconstruction Algorithm

Based on the static analysis, the trade-offs between accuracy and computation time in terms of N sensors and K ($\leq N$) modes are analyzed in Fig. 5.13: the blue circles in the top plot indicate the % errors of the reconstructed displacement field (relative to the FEA at the maximum value). The red dash-line indicates the upper bound of one standard deviation obtained from 100 tests with up to 10% Gaussian noise added to the simulated measurements to emulate environmental effects on sensed data. The solid-line in the bottom plot represents the time required to calculate one nodal displacement, and the standard deviations (plotted as error bars) are obtained with more than 3500 tests. All the measurements are taken at equally spaced locations along the referenced radius ($\theta = 0°$) of the constraint configuration in Fig. 5.12a with f_z applied at the radius center (95 mm, 0°) to represent a general

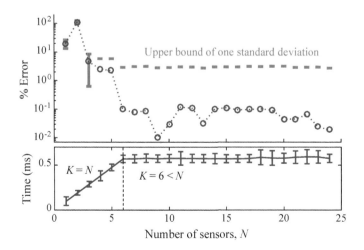

Fig. 5.13 Reconstruction efficiency

case where a focal force is exerted across the plate. The reconstruction is computed on a desktop computer (Intel i5 CPU 3.3 GHz, 8 GB RAM); for $N = 5$, it takes about 0.6 ms to calculate one reconstruction.

As shown in Fig. 5.13 (top), the error converges to less than 0.1% with more than five sensors, where the upper bound of the error is limited to 3%. Using the genetic algorithm in the MATLAB Optimization toolbox, the sensing locations are optimized by finding a proper modal coefficient matrix **S** that minimizes the condition number. With the optimized sensing locations, the reconstruction accuracy in Fig. 5.12 has been significantly improved as compared to that presented in our previous work [2] where the same number of sensors were used. Figure 5.13 (bottom) shows that the computation time increases linearly with N for $K = N$, and remains almost constant with increasing N for a specified $K = 6$; thus, the computation time required to reconstruct the displacement field is linearly dependent on K. As seen in (5.6), the reconstruction process involves linear algebraic superposition of K modes implying that more mode shapes for higher reconstruction accuracy would result in a larger modal coefficient matrix and thus longer calculation time. The aforementioned conclusions assume that all sensors are distributed equally in space; however, with optimized arrangement of sensor locations, higher reconstruction precision may be obtained with less number of sensors. As the focus here is to develop a reconstruction method, design optimization is briefly described in this work.

5.4 Experiment Results and Illustrative Application

The reconstruction of the displacement and strain fields has been experimentally evaluated on the machining testbed [2]. As shown in Fig. 5.14a where the world reference frame OXYZ is assigned at the rotation center, the inner portion ($r \leq b$) of a thin-wall plate (Table 5.1) is rigidly mounted on the motor shaft. The machining testbed was modified to allow non-contact measurements on one side of the workpiece (WP) and a displacement-input can be applied on the other side. The fields were reconstructed from a finite number of eddy-current sensors (ESs). To provide an alternative basis for experimental verification, a laser sensor and a pair of strain gauges (SG1 and SG2) were used for measurements of the displacement and strain respectively; however, the latter can only be used in a non-rotating plate experiment. With the sensor specifications detailed in Table 5.4, two experiments were conducted to validate the field reconstruction of the plate subjected to two different inputs; free vibration of a non-rotating plate (Fig. 5.14b) and lathe machining of a rotating WP (Fig. 5.14c).

5.4.1 Free Vibration of Non-rotating Plate

The non-rotating plate (Fig. 5.14b) was subjected to an initial deflection (w = 0.7 mm) specified by a micrometer which was suddenly released to simulate a step displacement-input at (X = 150 mm, Y = 0 mm). Two mode-shapes (K = 2) of the lowest orders were used for reconstruction from three eddy-current sensors (N = 3) so that the effects of the sensor locations on the reconstruction accuracy can be compared with the published results in [2]. The reconstructed dynamic displacement and strain fields were compared with real-time measurements (w; ε_{rr}, $\varepsilon_{\theta\theta}$) from

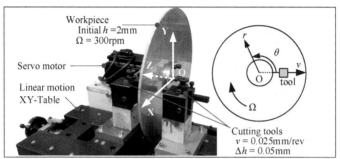

(a) Machining platform.

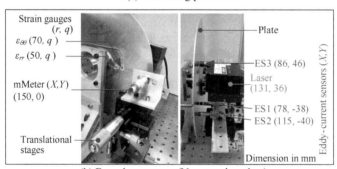

(b) Experiment setup (Non-rotating plate).

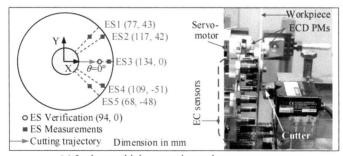

(c) Lathe-machining experimental measurement setup.

Fig. 5.14 Experimental setups

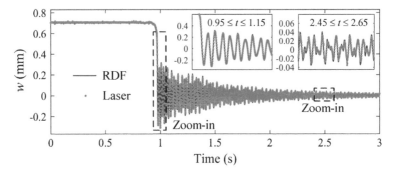

Fig. 5.15 Validation of the reconstructed displacement field (RDF)

the laser sensor and uniaxial strain gauges. As shown in Fig. 5.14b, the pair of strain gauges was aligned with the circumferential direction and along the radial direction to measure $\varepsilon_{\theta\theta}$ and ε_{rr}, respectively. The test was repeated multiple times with the same initial deflection to allow $(\varepsilon_{rr}, \varepsilon_{\theta\theta})$ measurements over a range of angular positions ($\theta = 0$ to $40°$ in step of $10°$). The results are presented in Figs. 5.15 and 5.16.

Figure 5.15 shows that the reconstructed displacement field (RDF) agrees well with the laser measurements, confirming the reconstruction can monitor the plate dynamics featured with multiple modes in real time. It is worth noting that the dominant vibration modes can only be captured by high-speed reconstruction that is generally limited by the sampling rate and calculation time. The sampling rate (2 kHz) employed here is high enough to capture the dominant modes while excluding other higher order modes in the reconstruction considering their negligible vibration amplitudes. With a computation speed faster than 1 kHz (Fig. 5.13), it is believed that this reconstruction method is sufficiently efficient for a broad range of structural dynamic problems in engineering.

In Fig. 5.16a, b, the reconstructed strain $(\varepsilon_{rr}, \varepsilon_{\theta\theta})$ fields are compared with the strain gauge measurements, where the error is defined as the difference between the reconstruction and measurement. The % errors are compared in Fig. 5.16c between two reconstructions of the same plate with different sensor locations where (r, θ) are measured in millimeters and degrees, respectively:

ES Set 1 (Fig. 5.14b): (78, −−38°), (115, −40°), (86, 46°)
ES Set 2 [2]: (100, −21°), (132, −16°), (106, 28°).

As shown in Fig. 5.16, all the normal strains respond in a similar fashion as the displacement because their linear relations (5.3) share the same modal coefficients (5.6). When θ changes from $40°$ to $0°$, ε_{rr} and $\varepsilon_{\theta\theta}$ increase from 1.2×10^{-4} to 1.9×10^{-4} and from 0.7×10^{-4} to 1.2×10^{-4}, respectively while their errors decrease from 2×10^{-5} to about 0.5×10^{-5} (with a lower % error at $0°$), which are consistent with the numerical error analysis in Fig. 5.12c. The error fluctuation in the static deflection tests was primarily caused by the noise of the strain gauges.

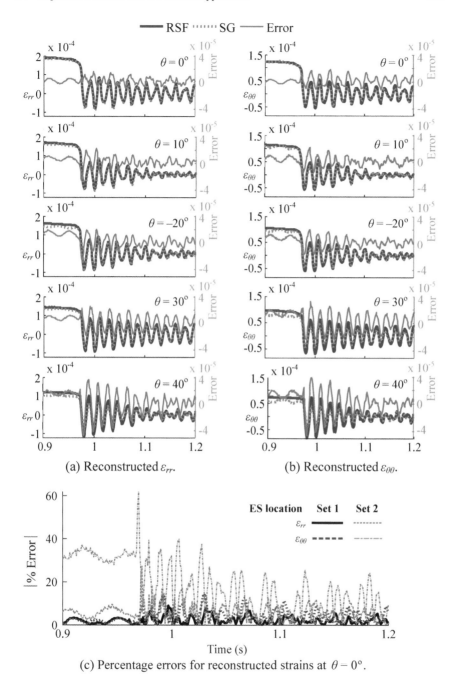

(a) Reconstructed ε_{rr}.

(b) Reconstructed $\varepsilon_{\theta\theta}$.

(c) Percentage errors for reconstructed strains at $\theta = 0°$.

Fig. 5.16 Reconstruction of time-varying strain distributions

The ES Set 1 results in a much smaller % errors than ES Set 2 in the normal strain reconstruction, suggesting that the errors can be reduced by optimizing the ES configuration.

5.4.2   Field Reconstruction for Machining

An aluminum plate (Table 5.1, $h = 1$ mm) was lathe-machined at the rotational speed Ω (=600 rpm) with the depth-of-cut Δh (=0.05 mm) and the tool feedrate v (=0.0125 mm/rev) from the inner edge towards the outer edge as shown in Fig. 5.14a, c where the pair of permanent magnets (located near the free edge) induces an eddy-current in the plate, which functions as a non-contact eddy-current damper (ECD) to reduce the WP vibration. The fields were reconstructed by superimposing three mode-shapes of the lowest orders ($K = 3$) from the displacement measurements of five nodal eddy-current sensors ($N = 5$). The constant depth-of-cut Δh, which is a small fraction ($\leq 1/2$ [3]) of the plate thickness, has little effects on the mode shapes. The fields were verified with the displacement measured by the sixed ES. Because the surface being machined was oily and partially obscured with chips as the cutter moves outward along $\theta = 0°$, the laser sensor was not used during cutting. The ability to

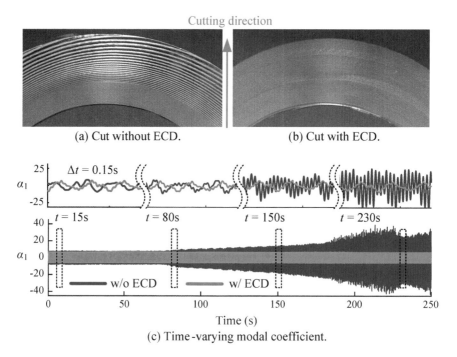

(a) Cut without ECD.   (b) Cut with ECD.

(c) Time-varying modal coefficient.

Fig. 5.17 Effect of eddy-current damper

account for the damping effects and external loads in the field reconstruction are demonstrated in Figs. 5.17, 5.18 and 5.19.

Figure 5.17a, b show qualitative comparison of the WP surfaces machined without and with the ECD respectively. The property of the modal coefficients that reflects the dynamic characteristics of the plate is illustrated in Fig. 5.17c where the dominant modal coefficients α_1's of the two cases (without/with ECD) are quantitatively compared. In Fig. 5.17c, the thin-dash rectangles indicate the time-intervals (0.l5 s each) of the zoom-in plots. The low-frequency α_1 variations in both (without/with ECD) cases are primarily due to the WP rotation, whereas the high-frequency variation (in the cutting without ECD) grows from the unstable machining dynamics. As shown in Fig. 5.17, the time-varying α_1 increasingly fluctuates with the actual depth-of-cut (closely related to the cutting force and WP vibration displacement) as the machined surface changes from smooth to rough during cutting without the ECD. As a comparison, a smaller and persistent variation of α_1 can be seen in the case of cutting with the ECD that effectively dissipates the high-frequency vibration energies yielding a relatively smooth surface.

Figure 5.18a, b show the ($N = 5$) ES measurements and the ($K = 3$) computed modal coefficients, which provide the basis for the reconstructed displacement and strains at the fixed point ($X = 94$ mm, $Y = 0$) in the reference coordinate in Fig. 5.18c. As shown in Fig. 5.18c, the reconstructed displacement at ($X = 94$ mm, $Y = 0$) excellently agrees with the ES measurements during machining (forced

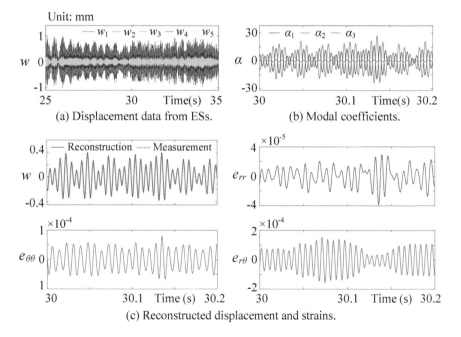

(a) Displacement data from ESs.

(b) Modal coefficients.

(c) Reconstructed displacement and strains.

Fig. 5.18 Reconstruction at (X, Y) = (94 mm, 0 mm) during machining

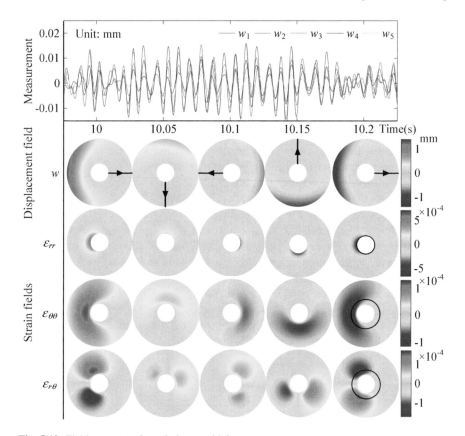

Fig. 5.19 Field reconstructions during machining

vibration with non-zero dampings). Figure 5.19 shows several snapshots of the displacement and strain fields along the timeline over one rotation period in the rotating frame, where the arrow indicates the cutting trajectory for rotation reference. Some observations about the validated field reconstruction in Fig. 5.19 are highlighted as follows:

- The maximum displacement is located on the opposite side of the cutting area. The most deflected point changing with the rotation period indicates that the intrinsic high-frequency plate dynamics is coupled with the low-frequency rotation, explaining that the low-frequency α_1 variations in Fig. 5.17c are primarily due to the workpiece rotation.
- The locations of the respective maximum strain values at each sampling time instance are marked in black and superimposed on the last-column plots. The maximum ε_{rr} occurs at the inner (clamped) edge, and the corresponding location is opposite to the cutting zone.

− The areas for the largest $\varepsilon_{\theta\theta}$ and $\varepsilon_{r\theta}$ are close to the inner edge, specifically about $r = 63.1$ mm. On the other hand, $\varepsilon_{\theta\theta}$ is zero along the clamped edge, and $\varepsilon_{r\theta}$ is zero along the diameter that is being cut.

More importantly, the in-situ field reconstruction provides a practical real-time feedback of the deflection at the cutting region (Fig. 5.19) for online compensation of the cutter motions; this relaxes the needs to measure the local WP displacement at the cutting point where stringent space limitations make direct measurements impractical. Additionally, the reconstruction offers a health diagnosis tool that monitors the maximum strains in the WP within its elastic range or its material yielding strain (5×10^{-4} for Al 1060) to prevent built-up of residual strains that is one of the main causes of distortions in final products. As indicated in Fig. 5.17c, the modal coefficient potentially plays the role of an alerting signal that monitors the displacement and strains within tolerances. The ability to locate maximum strains facilitates supplemental fixture designs to reduce residual stresses.

5.5 Summary

A plate dynamic model has been employed to capture the vibration characteristics of a thin-wall annular workpiece, where the effects of cutting process parameters (spindle speed and part thickness) on thin-wall workpiece dynamics have been verified numerically by comparing modal analysis with FEA results. An eddy-current sensing approach has been presented as a simple yet practical method for vibration measurements. Its sensing robustness and configuration have been investigated to provide a guideline to optimize sensor locations.

The field sensing method has been developed to reconstruct the continuous displacement/strain distributions across a flexible workpiece from a finite number of non-contact measurements during machining. Featured with simple implementation and high efficiency, this method has been numerically verified with FEA and experimentally validated on a flexible annular plate with a lathe machine testbed.

References

1. J. Guo, K. Lee, W. Liu, B. Wang, Design criteria based on modal analysis for vibration sensing of thin-wall plate machining. IEEE-ASME Trans. Mechatron. **20**(3), 1406–1417 (2015)
2. M. Yu, J. Guo, K.M. Lee, Strain field sensing and reconstruction for a thin-wall plate, in *Proceedings of the IEEE International Conference on Advanced Intelligent Mechatronics (AIM)*, Banff, Alberta, Canada, pp. 788–793 (2016)
3. J. Guo, R. Liu, K.-M. Lee, Dynamic modeling and analysis for thin-wall plate machining, in *Proceedings of the ASME Dynamic Systems and Control Conference*, Columbus, Ohio, USA, vol. 3 (2015)

Chapter 6
Bio-inspired Exoskeleton

Based on the bio-joint constraint formulated in Sect. 3.4, this chapter presents an anatomically-based knee model relaxing several commonly made assumptions that approximate a human knee as engineering pin-joint in exoskeleton design. Kinematics and dynamics are studied to investigate the effects of exoskeleton designs on the knee joint forces and torques. Then, an adaptive knee-joint exoskeleton is designed to eliminate negative effects associated with the closed leg-exoskeleton kinematic chain on a human knee.

6.1 Human Knee Kinematics

With MRI data, a model can be built to provide a good understanding of the kinematics and kinetics of a bio-joint (consisting of non-uniform shaped contact parts), and estimate its contact locations, rolling/sliding velocities and forces/torques involved. Figure 6.1 shows a lateral sagittal MRI of an unloaded cadaver knee [1], where the two white circles are approximated geometries for the femoral articular surfaces. Data are presented as positions of the extension facet center (EFC) and flexion facet center (FFC) in Fig. 6.1, where the contact is modeled as a point between a circle and a plane. To provide a continuous differentiable function, a general bio-joint representation based on elliptical geometries is proposed in Fig. 3.10 to characterize the observed data for analyzing the contact kinematics and kinetics, where Ω_A and Ω_B are two bodies with surfaces Γ_A and Γ_B respectively; and the angular velocity ω describes the motion of Ω_A rolling on Ω_B at the instantaneous contact point C.

In [1], two circles, each of which rolls on a different flat facet, were used for the sagittal section of the medial tibiofemoral compartment but for the lateral tibiofemoral compartment, two circles roll on the same flat facet. Here, the simulations focus on the lateral part as it has a larger displacement than the medial part. The following three models are compared:

© Huazhong University of Science and Technology Press, Wuhan and Springer Nature Singapore Pte Ltd. 2019
J. Guo and K.-M Lee, *Flexonics for Manufacturing and Robotics*, Research on Intelligent Manufacturing, https://doi.org/10.1007/978-981-13-2667-7_6

Fig. 6.1 MRI of a cadaver
knee

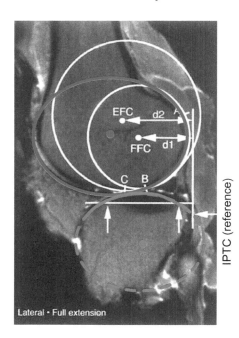

Model 1: Two sequential circles roll a flat plane [1].
Model 2: One ellipse rolls on a flat plane.
Model 3: One ellipse rolls on another ellipse.

The dimensions of the approximated circles and ellipses (Fig. 3.10) are listed in
Table 6.1. With the contact location defined as a horizontal distance of C measured
from the IPTC in Fig. 6.1, results are given as a function of the flexion angle θ in
Fig. 6.2 for comparing three models against the published data. Figure 6.3 simulates
(on the basis of Model 3) the snap-shot trajectory of the lower leg as it rotates from
its initially full extension, and its corresponding (rolling/sliding) displacements,
velocities as well as the s_{roll}/s_{slide} ratio.

Observations in Figs. 6.2 and 6.3 are discussed as follows:

(1) For Model 1, the s_{roll}/s_{slide} ratio is given as 1.7. As the sliding velocity of each
    rolling circle is assumed constant, the contact point is a linear function of θ. The

Table 6.1 Geometry approximation

Circles [1]		Ellipse (green dash)	
$r_1 = 21$ mm	$r_2 = 32$ mm	$r_{maj} = 25.3$ mm	$r_{min} = 21.1$ mm
Ellipse (blue)		Ellipse (red)	
$r_{maj} = 33.6$ mm	$r_{min} = 23$ mm	$r_{maj} = 28.8$ mm	$r_{min} = 18.8$ mm
Initial contact position = 31 mm			
Angular velocity $\omega = 1.57$ rad/s			

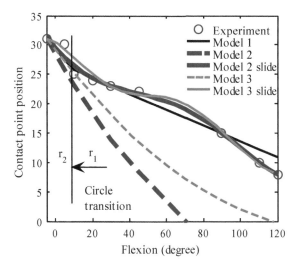

Fig. 6.2 Comparison of current contact point C

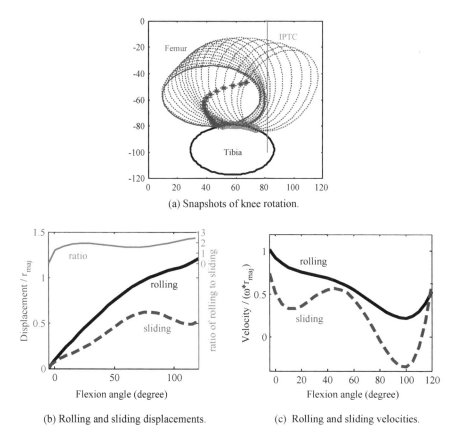

(a) Snapshots of knee rotation.

(b) Rolling and sliding displacements.   (c) Rolling and sliding velocities.

Fig. 6.3 Rolling and sliding velocities of the current contact point (Model 3)

overall result, however, is not a smooth curve (Fig. 6.2) due to the transition from circles r_2 to r_1.

The difference between the 2-circle model and experimental results can be observed when $\theta > 90°$. This is because the rotational axis of the circle is tilted by a small angle; when projected on the camera plane, the tilted circle is essentially as an ellipse.

(2) Based on the above observation, we model bio-joints using elliptical surfaces as they offer a more realistic characterization than a multi-circle model, and are mathematically differentiable.

Figure 6.2 compares Models 2 and 3 against the published data. With only rolling, Model 2 (that simplifies the tibial condyle as a planar surface) results in some negative contact positions; this is intuitively incorrect as the knee joint does not lose contact. Given the close match between Model 3 (when considering both sliding and rolling in the joint kinematics) and the experiment data, Model 3 with sliding is used for the subsequent analysis.

(3) The displacements, $s_{roll}(\theta)$ and $s_{slide}(\theta)$, normalized to the major radius of the femoral condyle, are given by (6.1a) and (6.1b) respectively, and their ratio is plotted in Fig. 3b:

$$s_{roll}(\theta)/r_{maj} = 0.093\theta^5 - 0.409\theta^4 + 0.57\theta^3 - 0.448\theta^2 + 0.926\theta \qquad (6.1a)$$

$$s_{slide}(\theta)/r_{maj} = 0.334\theta^5 - 1.518\theta^4 + 2.12\theta^3 - 0.996\theta^2 + 0.513\theta \qquad (6.1b)$$

The s_{roll}/s_{slide} ratio is not a constant, but its average value of 1.69 closely agrees with the experimental observation [1] of 1.7. Figure 6.3c graphs v_{slide} by differentiating (6.1); negative v_{slide} means sliding forward instead of backward.

6.2 Knee Joint Dynamics

The calf dynamics (relative to the upper leg) are given by (6.2):

$$m\mathbf{a} = \mathbf{f}_g + \mathbf{f}_\theta + \mathbf{f}_r + \mathbf{f}_e \qquad (6.2a)$$

$$(J\ddot{\theta} + 2mr\dot{r}\dot{\theta})\mathbf{k} = \tau_g + \tau_a + \tau_e \quad \text{where } \mathbf{k} = \mathbf{e}_r \times \mathbf{e}_\theta \qquad (6.2b)$$

In (6.2a), m is the calf mass; $\mathbf{f}_g$ is the gravity force; and $\mathbf{f}_r$ and $\mathbf{f}_\theta$ are the resultant forces exerted by the surrounding bones and tissues (muscle and ligament) in $\mathbf{e}_r$ and $\mathbf{e}_\theta$ directions respectively. Within a bio-joint, bones primarily support compressive forces, and soft tissues can only exert tensile forces. For example, $\mathbf{f}_r$ represents the force from the tissues if tensile force dominates, or otherwise from the bones. With rehabilitation applications in mind, we include $\mathbf{f}_e$ to account for the force exerted by an external device (such as an exoskeleton) and reaction from the ground. On the left hand side of (6.2b), the first term accounts for the moment-of-inertia J (about the initial contact point C_i) due to the leg rotation while the second term describes the interaction between $\dot{\theta}$ and $\dot{r}$ due to the variation in r. In (6.2b), all the torques are computed about C_i: τ_g and τ_e denote the torques due to the gravity and external device respectively; and τ_a is a net torque accounting for $\mathbf{f}_r$, $\mathbf{f}_\theta$ and tissue contraction within the knee.

The vector Eq. (6.2) can be recast into three scalar Eq. (6.3) from which f_r, f_θ and τ_a can be solved:

$$m\left(\ddot{r} - r\dot{\theta}^2\right) = f_g \sin\theta + f_r + f_{er}(\theta) \qquad (6.3a)$$

$$m(2\dot{r}\dot{\theta} + r\ddot{\theta}) = f_g \cos\theta + f_\theta + f_{e\theta}(\theta) \qquad (6.3b)$$

$$J\ddot{\theta} + 2mr\dot{r}\dot{\theta} = \tau_g + \tau_a + \tau_e(\theta) \qquad (6.3c)$$

Due to the kinematic constraint imposed by the contact, the human knee joint embodies two DOFs, rotation and translation for its planar motion. To investigate the effects of a planar exoskeleton on human knee joints, we compare two different models in predicting the forces and moments acting on the knee; namely,

- pin joint engineering approximation, and
- bio-joint knee (Model 3).

The exoskeleton consists of a revolute (pin) joint between two rigid links attached to the lower and upper legs with pin joints. This design has three-DOF from its three pin-joints and thus has one redundancy. For a nonzero flexion angle, there are two possible solutions. However, only one solution is physically feasible.

For clarity and ease of illustration, the following assumptions are made; (1) the human subject sits with the upper leg held static and horizontal and the lower link rotates with the tibia from its initial state (full extension); and (2) the lower link is attached at O with the revolute joint centered at the initial contact point C_i (Fig. 6.4). Numerical values used in this study are given in Table 6.2 [2] and from Figs. 6.4b and 6.3a,

$$r(\theta) = 1.078\theta^4 - 11.184\theta^3 + 26.542\theta^2 - 0.825\theta + 263.59 \qquad (6.4)$$

Equation (6.4) and its derivatives are graphed in Fig. 6.5. Figure 6.6 shows the link kinematics (solid lines) as the tibia rotates, where dash lines simulate the knee as a pin joint (commonly assumed in exoskeleton designs) for comparison.

To account for the exoskeleton mass in the kinetic study, the two links are assumed to have the same mass-to-length ratio η of 0.5 kg/m. Unlike the condition with no exoskeleton where the human leg is an open-chain mechanism, the leg and exoskeleton form a closed kinematic chain that has a significant effect on the internal joint forces and torque of the knee. Figure 6.7 are calculated results from

Fig. 6.4 Coordinates illustrating the knee joint rotation

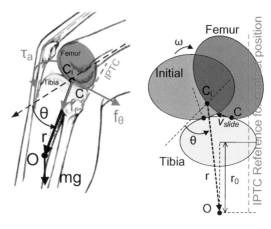

(a) Tibia rotation.   (b) Schematics illustration.

Table 6.2 Physical parameters of human's lower leg

	Human		Exoskeleton
	Length (m)	Mass (kg)	Length (m)
Upper leg	0.40	7.02	0.40
Lower leg/foot	0.37/0.27	2.44/1.18	0.37
r_0 (m)	0.2453		

Fig. 6.5 Kinematics of the tibia mass-center

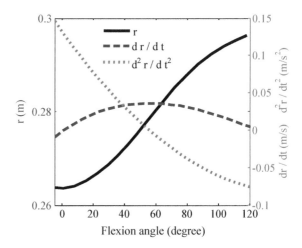

(6.3) showing the internal forces and torque in the knee as the tibia accelerates from the initial static state ($\theta = -5°$) to $\theta = 20°$ for 0.5 s, then maintains at an angular velocity for 1 s to $\theta = 95°$, and finally decelerates to the final static state $\theta = 115°$ in another 0.5 s. Throughout the trajectory, the foot is off the ground and thus, there is no ground reaction. In Fig. 6.7 where the thick and thin lines are results of the

Fig. 6.6 Comparing
snapshots of an exoskeleton
between two knee joint
models

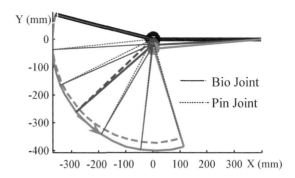

bio-joint and pin joint models respectively, the internal forces and torque for a
condition with no exoskeleton are plotted as a basis for comparison.

Several observations can be made in Figs. 6.5, 6.6 and 6.7:

(1) The sign of the force f_r in Fig. 6.7a can be explained as follows. During the
initial flexion ($\theta < 0$), f_r is positive since the force is primarily supported by the
femur, but becomes negative as the retraction force from the soft tissues
gradually plays a more dominant role as the knee rotates downward.

(2) The distance r increases as much as 30 mm (Fig. 6.5). For the same work done,
this increase in r tends to reduce f_r in the knee. As the pin joint approximation
assumes a constant r and neglects the joint geometry, the effect of the $r(\theta)$
variation on the attaching point (Fig. 6.6) and on the forces/torque (Fig. 6.7)
cannot be accounted for. As compared to the bio-joint model in Fig. 6.7a, the
pin joint approximation overestimates $|f_r|$ in the range ($0° < \theta < 90°$) and
underestimates as θ approaches its rotation limit.

(3) Near $\theta = 0°$, the exoskeleton loses one DOF along the $\mathbf{e_r}$ direction causing a finite
change in f_r as well as f_θ and τ_a as shown in Fig. 6.7. Human knee (that can roll
and slide) is more tolerant than a pin-joint to a singularity along $\mathbf{e_r}$ as illustrated in
Fig. 6.7a. However, these internal forces and torque increase with the
mass-to-length ratio η of the exoskeleton. An increase in η from 0.5 to 1 kg/m
implies that f_r (at $\theta = 0^-$, $\theta = 0^+$) would increase from (39, −24 N) to
(73, −51 N). The pin joint approximation, which neglects the $r(\theta)$ variation,
cannot capture the finite change in f_r and also grossly underestimates the singularity effect on f_θ and τ_a.

(4) The trapezoidal-velocity θ trajectory (commonly used in robotics) has an effect
on the tangential force f_θ and moment τ_a. As seen in Fig. 6.7b, c, the two
sudden changes at $\theta = 20°$ and $\theta = 95°$ (on the simulated f_θ and τ_a) are reac-
tions from the soft tissues in order to meet the acceleration changes specified in
the θ trajectory.

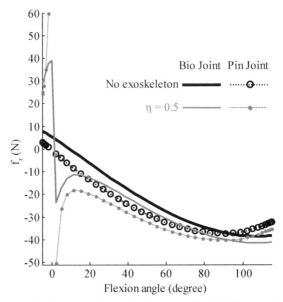

(a) Pin-joint knee approximation overestimates f_r in the range $-5° < \theta < 90°$ and underestimated in $\theta > 90°$ as compared to the bio-joint knee model.

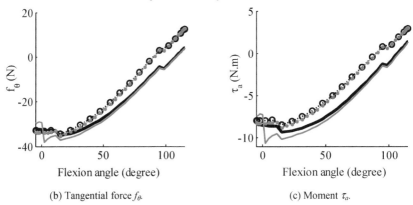

(b) Tangential force f_θ.   (c) Moment τ_a.

Fig. 6.7 Force and torque comparison between two knee joint models (with/without exoskeleton)

6.3   Knee-Exoskeleton Coupling

Figure 6.8 shows a typical knee-exoskeleton (K-E) structure with the upper link and leg held stationary at a horizontal position while the knee flexes (angle θ) under gravity. As shown in Fig. 6.8a, the lower link rotates (angle φ) about the pin joint C_e, and slides (displacement u) relative to the attaching point E fixed on the lower leg; and u is defined to be zero at $\theta = 0$, so that the point "o" on the lower link overlaps with E.

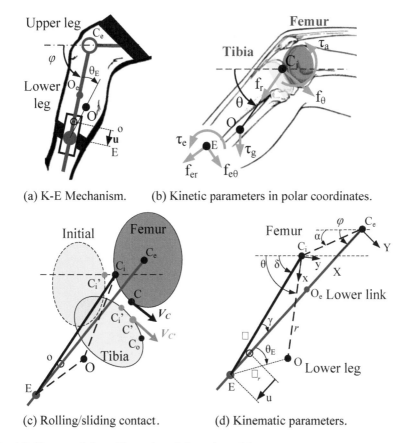

(a) K-E Mechanism.   (b) Kinetic parameters in polar coordinates.

(c) Rolling/sliding contact.   (d) Kinematic parameters.

Fig. 6.8 Knee-exoskeleton kinematic and dynamic models

Using a lumped-parameter approach in the polar coordinate (r, θ) with its origin at C_i, the motion of the lower leg (mass m, moment of inertia J) can be described by the displacement of its mass-center O as shown in Fig. 6.8b, where τ_e is the actuating torque of the exoskeleton; $(f_{er}, f_{e\theta})$ are the forces exerted by the exoskeleton at E (along and perpendicular to the lower link); (f_r, f_θ) and τ_a denote the internal forces/torque exerted by the femur on the tibia in the knee, respectively; and τ_g is the torque due to the gravitational force mg (or the weight) of the lower leg. For investigating the effects of exoskeleton designs on a knee, the relative motion of the lower link (m_e, J_e) to the lower leg is characterized by the displacement u of the mass-center O_e and the angle θ_E between EO_e and EO.

Figure 6.8c shows a separated bio-joint coupled with an exoskeleton link C_eE, where C_i and C_i' are initial contact points on the femur and tibia respectively, C and C' are instantaneous contact points and C_o is instantaneous contact point when the joint rolls purely. As the lower leg flexes ($\theta > 0$), the tibia rolls and slides on the femur. The instantaneous rotation axis of the knee moves with the tibia as illustrated in Fig. 6.8c. Because C_i and C_e are non-concentric, the line-vector $\mathbf{P}_i$ (C_i to E) and its orientation δ change as geometrically shown in Fig. 6.8d.

It is desired that the K-E bio-mechatronic structure works with constant u and θ_E while the lower leg flexes, and that the user experiences minimum internal forces/torque (f_r, f_θ, τ_a). To minimize the kinematic deviations and hence the internal forces and torque in the knee, the displacement between C_e and E on the exoskeleton must be made adaptable in design.

6.3.1 Coupled Kinematics

To facilitate the following discussions, the reference coordinate system XY is assigned at C_e on the exoskeleton with its X-axis pointing along the lower link as shown in Fig. 6.8d; and the coordinate system xy at C_i on the femur with its x-axis pointing towards the centroid of the lower leg. The coordinate transformation from xy to XY frames is given by (6.5) where l_i is the distance between C_i and C_e:

$$\mathbf{P} = [\mathbf{R}(z, \theta - \varphi)]\mathbf{p} + \mathbf{P}_i \tag{6.5}$$

where
$$[\mathbf{R}(z, \theta - \varphi)] = \begin{bmatrix} \cos(\theta - \varphi) & -\sin(\theta - \varphi) \\ \sin(\theta - \varphi) & \cos(\theta - \varphi) \end{bmatrix}$$
and

$$\mathbf{P}_i = \begin{bmatrix} X_i \\ Y_i \end{bmatrix} = \begin{bmatrix} l_i \cos(\varphi - \alpha) \\ -l_i \sin(\varphi - \alpha) \end{bmatrix}.$$

For a given design, $\mathbf{P}_i$ (or the location C_i) is calibrated as will be described in Sect. 6.4 and thus l_i and α are assumed known.

A. *Forward kinematics*

Given the angular displacement φ of the exoskeleton, the forward kinematics of the knee-exoskeleton mechanism solves for the knee angle $\theta(\varphi)$, the displacement $u(\varphi)$ and the torque angle $\theta_E(\varphi)$ in terms of the calibrated contact point C_i for a specified geometry (O, E, C_e, ℓ_E, ℓ and ℓ_E):

$$\mathbf{P}_E = \begin{bmatrix} \ell_E + u \\ 0 \end{bmatrix} = \begin{bmatrix} \ell \cos(\delta - \varphi) + l_i \cos(\varphi - \alpha) \\ \ell \sin(\delta - \varphi) - l_i \sin(\varphi - \alpha) \end{bmatrix} \tag{6.6a}$$

$$\mathbf{P}_O = \begin{bmatrix} X_O \\ Y_O \end{bmatrix} = \begin{bmatrix} r \cos(\theta - \varphi) + l_i \cos(\varphi - \alpha) \\ r \sin(\theta - \varphi) - l_i \sin(\varphi - \alpha) \end{bmatrix} \tag{6.6b}$$

$$r = |\mathbf{P}_O - \mathbf{P}_i| \tag{6.6c}$$

The knee flexion angle can be derived from (6.6b):

$$\theta(\varphi) = \cos^{-1}\left(\frac{X_O - \ell_i \cos(\varphi - \alpha)}{r}\right) + \varphi \tag{6.7}$$

Using the cosine law for the triangle $\Delta C_i E C_e$ in Fig. 6.8d,

$$u(\varphi) = \sqrt{\ell^2 + \ell_i^2 - 2\ell\ell_i \cos(\pi - \delta + \alpha)} - \ell_E \tag{6.8}$$

where $\ell = \ell_i \frac{\sin(\varphi - \alpha)}{\sin(\delta - \varphi)}$. Similarly, using the sine law for $\Delta C_i E O$ in Fig. 6.8d,

$$\theta_E(\varphi) = \sin^{-1}\left(\frac{r \sin(\theta - \varphi - \gamma)}{|\mathbf{P}_E - \mathbf{P}_O|}\right) - \gamma \tag{6.9}$$

where $\gamma = \delta - \varphi = \sin^{-1}\left(\frac{\ell_i}{l}\sin(\varphi - \alpha)\right)$.

B. *Inverse kinematics*

The inverse kinematics solves for the exoskeleton flexion angle $\varphi(\theta)$ for a desired knee flexion angle which can be solved from (6.6b):

$$\varphi(\theta) = \cos^{-1}\left(\frac{(r \cos\theta + \ell_i \cos\alpha)X_O + (r \sin\theta + \ell_i \sin\alpha)Y_O}{r^2 + \ell_i^2 + 2r\ell_i \cos(\theta - \alpha)}\right) \tag{6.10}$$

6.3.2 Coupled Dynamics

The equations governing the dynamics of lower leg and link are given in (6.11) and (6.12) respectively, which provide a basis for investigating the effects of different exoskeleton designs on the internal forces and torque (f_r, f_θ, τ_a) in the knee:

$$m(\ddot{r} - r\dot{\theta}^2) = mg \sin\theta + f_r + f_{er}\cos(\theta - \varphi) + f_{e\theta}\sin(\theta - \varphi) \tag{6.11a}$$

$$m(2\dot{r}\dot{\theta} + r\ddot{\theta}) = mg \cos\theta + f_\theta - f_{er}\sin(\theta - \varphi) + f_{e\theta}\cos(\theta - \varphi) \tag{6.11b}$$

$$J\ddot{\theta} + 2mr\dot{r}\dot{\theta} = \tau_g + \tau_a + \tau_e - f_{er}l \sin\gamma + f_{e\theta}l \cos\gamma \tag{6.11c}$$

$$m_e(\ddot{r}_e - r_e\dot{\varphi}^2) = m_e g \sin\varphi + f_l \cos\varepsilon - f_{er} - f_m \cos(\varphi + \eta) \tag{6.12a}$$

$$m_e(2\dot{r}_e\dot{\varphi} + r_e\ddot{\varphi}) = m_e g \cos\varphi - f_l \sin\varepsilon - f_{e\theta} + f_m \sin(\varphi + \eta) - f_d \tag{6.12b}$$

$$J_e\ddot{\varphi} + 2m_e r_e\dot{r}_e\dot{\varphi} = \tau_{ge} - f_{e\theta}(l_E + u) - \tau_e - \tau_m - \tau_f - \tau_l \tag{6.12c}$$

The torques and moments-of-inertia in the third equations of (6.11) and (6.12) are computed about the rotation axes at C_i and C_e, respectively. For a given exoskeleton,

$$f_{er} = -k_r u - \mu f_{e\theta} \text{sign}(\dot{u}) \tag{6.13}$$

$$\tau_e = k_\theta (\theta_E - \theta_{E(0)}) \tag{6.14}$$

where $\dot{u}$ is the velocity of point E; $\theta_{E(0)}$ is the initial value of θ_E; and μ is the friction coefficient of the end slider. In (6.12c), τ_{ge} is the torque acting on the lower link due to gravity; τ_f is the friction torque; (f_m, τ_m) are the actuating force/torque of the exoskeleton on the lower-link; (f_l, τ_l) are the contact force/torque of the cam roller in the cam mechanism; f_d is the contact force of the slider in the cam mechanism; and the angles (ε and η) characterize the force direction of the cam-slot and motor.

6.4   Experimental Investigation

The objectives of the experimental study are (1) to validate the kinematics of the knee-exoskeleton closed-chain mechanism; (2) to analyze the tibia rolling and sliding on a femur; (3) to investigate the effects of different exoskeleton design configurations on the knee internal forces and torque; and (4) to examine the feasibility of accommodating a limited range of size/shape variations with the method of adaptive knee-joint exoskeleton.

6.4.1   Design Configurations

Five design configurations (with calculated *DOFs*) along with a human knee-joint flexing freely without any exoskeleton are compared in Table 6.3. The case without exoskeleton provides a basis for numerical investigating the effect of the exoskeleton designs on the internal forces (f_r, f_θ) and torque τ_a in the knee.

*DC*1 (Pin and fixed end)	The link is connected by engineering pin-joint to the fixed brace; r_e is a constant in (6.12) because links are inextensible. However, these rigid links cannot adapt to the varying distance r (as has been discussed in [3]), the attachment E is thus subjected to compression, extension and torsion.
*DC*2 (Pin and slider)	The link slides with respect to the leg brace to accommodate for the knee-joint translational motion in e_r direction relieving the compression at E; $k_r = 0$.

Table 6.3 Specifications of exoskeleton designs

No exoskeleton (DOFs = 2)	(*DC*1, DOFs = 0)	(*DC*2, DOFs = 1)
	$k_r \to \infty,\ k_\theta \to \infty$	$k_r \to 0,\ k_\theta \to \infty$
(*DC*3, DOFs = 1)	(*DC*4, DOFs = 2)	(*DC*5, DOFs = 2)
$k_r \to 0,\ k_\theta \to \infty$	$k_r \to 0,\ k_\theta \to 0$	$k_r \to 0,\ k_\theta \to 0$

*DC*3 (Cam and slider)	To account for the non-uniform geometry of the biological knee joint, the hinge in *DC*2 is replaced by a grooved cam allowing the link length r_e to vary with respect to the cam profile during motion.
*DC*4 (Pin and pinned slider)	The hinge in *DC*4 allows for sliding and rotating to accommodate the torque angle θ_E between the link and leg; $k_\theta = 0$ because a hinge cannot transmit torques.
*DC*5 (Cam and pinned slider)	The hinge in *DC*5 is allowed to slide and rotate. Combined with a grooved cam, this design can accommodate changes of both the distance r and the torque angle θ_E.

6.4.2 Experimental Test Bed

Figure 6.9a shows the experimental test bed built upon an existing lower-extremity rehabilitation exoskeleton (LERE) [4]. As illustrated in Fig. 6.9a, b which shows the CAD model and the photograph of the prototype adaptive exoskeleton, respectively, the cam mechanism is made up of two assemblies which move relative to each other through a revolute joint; namely, a pair of connecting plates fixed on the upper-link at C_e (each of which has a machined slot characterizing the cam profile), and a connecting bar (with a linear slot) rigidly attached to the lower link. As the lower link rotates, the rollers (fixed on the connecting bar) follow the slotted cam profile between the pair of connecting plates, while its cam center C_e (pin with sleeves) is allowed to slide along the linear slot of the connecting bar.

To investigate the effects of geometrical size/shape variations on the knee-exoskeleton interaction, an artificial model (A82 Functional Knee Joint Model, 3B Scientific GmbH, Germany) was chosen for emulating the knee joint mechanics in experiments as shown in Fig. 6.9c. The artificial model is smaller than the human knee [1] from which the models were derived to perform hardware-in-the-loop simulation. To facilitate validation, two markers are placed at the mass-center O located experimentally and calibrated Ci for directly measuring the displacement r, the images of which can be captured with a camera for off-line analysis. A rotary joint is added at the end attachment (see point E in Fig. 6.8) to compensate for the angular deviation between the lower leg and the exoskeleton link. Different configurations can be investigated by engaging or disengaging some kinematic pairs. The displacement u was measured by a cable-driven potentiometer. Four force sensors (Honeywell piezo-resistive FSG-15N1 A) were used to measure f_{er} and $f_{e\theta}$.

6.4.3 Experimental Methods

In solving the kinematics and dynamics of a K-E mechanism, the point of attachment E is known. As the lower leg can be separated from the knee joint, its mass center O can be located by a force plate method [5], and thus (X_O, Y_O) can be defined after reassembly. The angle δ can be described by a polynomial function of the knee flexion angle θ [3]; for the knee joint,

$$\delta = \theta - 0.078$$

However, the following unknowns must be calibrated:

(1) Location C_i (characterized by the distance ℓ_i and angle α) which provides a basis to determine the displacement of the mass-center O as a function of flexion, $r(\theta)$.

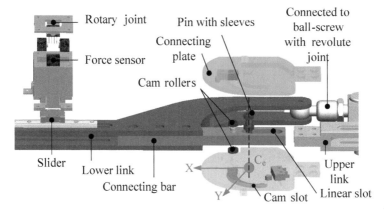

(a) Cam mechanism CAD exploded view.

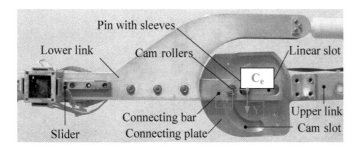

(b) Cam mechanism used in experimental setup.

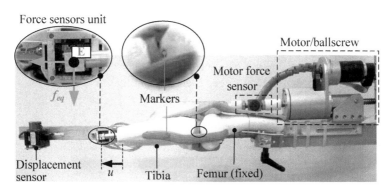

(c) An artificial knee joint attached on the lower-link.

Fig. 6.9 Experimental setup

(2) Rolling/sliding displacements in the knee. These contact conditions are essential for simulating the closed kinematic chain motion of the K-E structure.
(3) Design parameters of the cam profile for $DC3$ and $DC5$, which depends on specific knee size.

The calibration of the initial contact point C_i (on the femur) and the rolling/sliding displacements of the knee-joint were performed experimentally using exoskeleton $DC4$.

A. *Calibration for initial contact point* C_i

Since $\ell_E + u$ is measurable, the X-component term of (6.6a) is expanded for use as a basis for calibrating ℓ_i and α:

$$[\cos\varphi + \cot(\delta - \varphi)\sin\varphi]\ell_i\cos\alpha + [\sin\varphi - \cot(\delta - \varphi)\cos\varphi]\ell_i\sin\alpha = \ell_E + u$$
$$(6.15)$$

As the K-E mechanism flexes a full range, data can be collected and organized into a system of linear equations of the form:

$$[\mathbf{A}]\mathbf{Z} = \mathbf{b} \tag{6.16}$$

where $[\mathbf{A}] = \begin{bmatrix} a_{11} & a_{12} \\ \vdots & \vdots \\ a_{k1} & a_{k2} \\ \vdots & \vdots \\ a_{n1} & a_{n2} \end{bmatrix}$, $[\mathbf{b}] = \begin{bmatrix} l_E + u_1 \\ \vdots \\ l_E + u_k \\ \vdots \\ l_E + u_n \end{bmatrix}$, $\mathbf{Z} = \begin{bmatrix} l_i\cos\alpha \\ l_i\sin\alpha \end{bmatrix}$,

$a_{k1} = \cos\varphi_k + \cot(\delta_k - \varphi_k)\sin\varphi_k$, $a_{k2}\sin\varphi_k - \cot(\delta_k - \varphi_k)\cos\varphi_k$.

Using a least-square method minimizing the fitting errors, the solution to the over-determined system (6.16) can be obtained from the pseudo-inverse:

$$\mathbf{Z} = [\mathbf{A}^T\mathbf{A}]^{-1}\mathbf{A}^T\mathbf{b} \tag{6.17}$$

Once $\mathbf{Z}$ is solved the location C_i (l_i and α) can be calculated

$$\ell_i = \sqrt{z_1^2 + z_2^2},\ \alpha = \tan^{-1}(z_2/z_1) \tag{6.18}$$

B. *Knee rolling/sliding displacements*

The computation of the displacements follows three steps.

Step 1   Obtains the pure rolling distance S_p assuming that the tibia rolls purely on the femur without any sliding:

$$S_p = \int \rho d\theta \tag{6.19}$$

where ρ is the radius of an osculating circle.

Step 2   Initializes a search point C' on the tibia that would correspond to an instantaneous C on the femur.

Step 3   Optimizes the search point C' with two constraint functions (6.20) along with a least-square objective function (6.21) for mass-center O of the lower-leg:

$$\mathbf{V}_c = \mathbf{V}_{c'} \text{ and } C = C' \tag{6.20}$$

$$\text{Min} \sum \{r - r_a\}^2 \tag{6.21}$$

where $\mathbf{V}_c$ and $\mathbf{V}_{c'}$ are the tangent vectors of the coincident points C and C' respectively; and r_a is determined by tibia position/orientation based on the chosen point C'.

With the tibia rolls and slides on the femur, the rolling distance S_r (from C_i to C on the femur, which is also equal to the arc-length from C_i' to C_o on the tibia) and the sliding distance S_s (from C' to C_o on the tibia) are in analyzing the dynamics in a knee joint:

$$S_r = \widehat{C_iC} \text{ and } S_s = \widehat{C'C_o} \tag{6.22a, b}$$

C. *Cam profile design*

Modified with a scaling factor "a" and the cam-shape factor "s", the cam profile based on the model of a human knee-joint [3] for $DC3$ and $DC5$ takes the form given as

$$C_p = a\theta(1.078\theta^3 - 11.184\theta^2 + 26.542\theta - 0.825) + s \tag{6.23}$$

The two design parameters (a and s) depend on the knee size and shape to be determined experimentally.

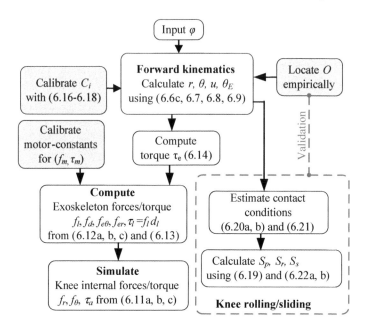

Fig. 6.10 Flowchart illustrating the computation of the analytical model

Table 6.4 Specifications of the lower leg and link

Parameters	Lower leg	Lower link	
		DC1, 2, 4	DC3, 5
ℓ or ℓ_E (mm)	157.5	161	161
Effective link mass center		$r_e = 158.5$	$r_e = 143.6$
m or m_e (kg)	0.164	0.5439	0.5692
J or J_e (kg m^2)	5.68×10^{-4}	2.069×10^{-2}	1.858×10^{-2}
Mean τ_f (N m)	Neglected	0.025	0.029
Knee joint	r_{maj} (mm)	r_{min} (mm)	
Femur	23.3	15.9	
Tibia	19.9	13	
Attachments	$k_r = 8000$ N/m; $k_\theta = 0.5$ N m/rad		
Friction coefficient		$\mu = 0.2$	

6.4.4   Results and Discussion

The computational steps are illustrated in Fig. 6.10 along with the parametric values used in the simulation are listed in Table 6.4. Since the internal knee forces and torque cannot be directly measured, they are computed from (6.11) with experimentally measured exoskeleton internal forces and torque.

Fig. 6.11 Verification of computed mass-center displacements

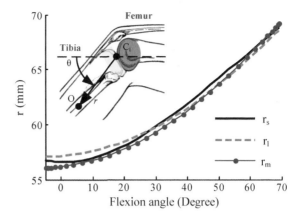

Three sets of results are presented. The first set determines the values of the characteristic parameters, and validates the closed kinematic-chain model of the K-E structure by comparing the measured lower-leg mass-center displacement against the simulated result. The second set determines the rolling and sliding displacements of the knee joint. The third set investigates the effects of different exoskeleton design configurations on the knee internal forces and torque.

A. *Validation of K-E Closed Kinematic-chain Model*

Using (6.16)–(6.18), the location of initial contact point C_i on the femur was experimentally calibrated on the $DC4$ K-E mechanism; $\mathbf{P}_i = [X_i\ Y_i]^{\mathrm{T}} =$ [3.5 6.0] in mm. The mass-center displacement $r(\theta)$ can be computed from the distance between C_i and O using (6.6b); the results presented by a curved-fit is given in (6.24a):

$$r_l = -0.80\theta^4 + 0.93\theta^3 + 6.80\theta^2 + 1.33\theta + 57.13 \qquad (6.24a)$$

To illustrate the results and validate the models, results of (6.24a) are verified against two sets of data; published and experimentally measured data:

$r_s(\theta)$: published data [3] based on knee geometry scaled from a nominal model without considering the specific details of the artificial knee joint.

$$r_s = a\theta(1.08\theta^3 - 11.18\theta^2 + 26.54\theta - 0.825) + 56.6 \qquad (6.24b)$$

$r_m(\theta)$: experimental data obtained using markers placed on the lower leg and captured with a camera.

$$r_m = -0.84\theta^4 + 0.83\theta^3 + 7.59\theta^2 + 1.86\theta + 56.18 \qquad (6.24c)$$

The scaling factors in (6.24b) are identified to be $a = 0.6$. The results are compared in Fig. 6.11. All the three sets of results closely agree with each other.

With the coordinate system established for this setup, full extension of a knee joint implies negative angle of the tibia orientation. The negative initial value ($-5°$) of the flexion angle θ (horizontal axis) is determined from the bio-joint kinematic model in [3] and MRI images obtained in [1].

B. *Knee Rolling/sliding Displacement Analysis*

With calibrated C_i and mass-center displacement $r_l(\theta)$, the rolling/sliding displacements (and thus the contact points C and C_i') as the tibia rolls and slides on the fixed femur are computed from (6.19) to (6.22) and simulated in Figs. 6.11 and 6.12.

Figure 6.12a shows the calculated displacements of the lower-leg mass-center O, which agree well with measurements with an average error of 1.87 mm and a maximum difference of 2.59 mm (1.7% of the tibia length or less than 5% of the motion range). The displacements of the initial contact point C_i' (on tibia) in the y direction also agree well with experimental data in Fig. 6.12b. The relative effects of the rolling and sliding as knee flexes can be analyzed in Fig. 6.13 showing that when $\theta < 30°$, the tibia motion relative to femur is mostly rolling; after $\theta > 30°$, sliding appears while rolling gradually decreases. These results, which are also consistent with the qualitative conclusion in [6] that rolling is dominant at the beginning of flexion, and sliding becomes dominant as knee flexes, validate the calculations of knee-joint kinematics.

C. *Cam Profile Designs*

The design of the cam profile has been based on two considerations. The first consideration is to account for individual size/shape variations by means of scaling and cam-shape factors based on the knee joint geometry provided in [1, 3]. The second consideration is to design the cam profile with a flat contact area (at zero flexion angle) to support the weight of the human and exoskeleton when standing. For these considerations, the effect of the correction factor "s" in (6.23) is analyzed by comparing two cam profiles in Fig. 6.14a against that with $s = 0$:

$$C1: \quad s = 25\cos(\varphi + 0.0873)$$
$$C2: \quad s = 15$$

The profile $C1$ is designed to accommodate the change in r due to the non-uniform geometry; while $C2$ offers similar compensation as $C1$ but includes a flat contact area at zero flexion angle to support the weight of the human and exoskeleton when standing. As compared in Fig. 6.14a, $C2$ has a larger range of flatness in the neighborhood of $\varphi \in [-2°, 2°]$ than $C1$. The displacement u is also calculated in Fig. 6.14b based on the experimental result of r_l and (6.8). As shown in the aforementioned results, the cam profile $C2$ can diminish the relative motion of the exoskeleton lower link to the human lower leg, and thus chosen for the remaining research investigation and the following discussions.

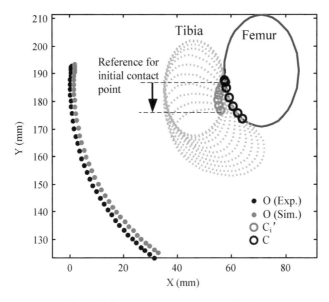

(a) Rolling/sliding and mass-center displacements

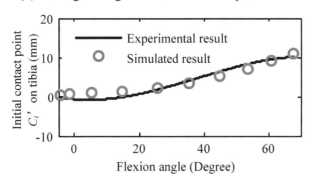

(b) Initial contact point on tibia, y-component displacement

Fig. 6.12 Experiment and simulated contact kinematics in a knee joint

D. *Effect of Exoskeleton on Internal Forces/Torque*

Simulated and experimental results of the five design configurations are compared against the case without exoskeleton in Figs. 6.15, 6.16 and Table 6.5 where the mean, root-mean-square (RMS) and maximum values of the knee internal forces or torque are compared quantitatively.

Deviations between experiment and simulation results in Figs. 6.15 and 6.16 could be due to two possible causes; the mass-center location and model approximation. As compared in Fig. 6.12a, the maximum difference in the mass centers is only 1.7% of the length of tibia; this relatively small difference which may be due to

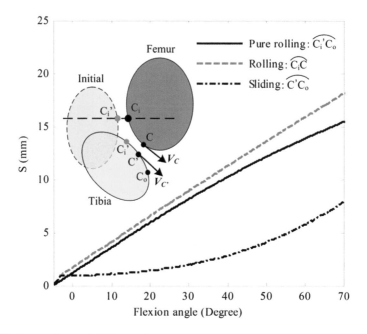

Fig. 6.13 Knee rolling and sliding analyses

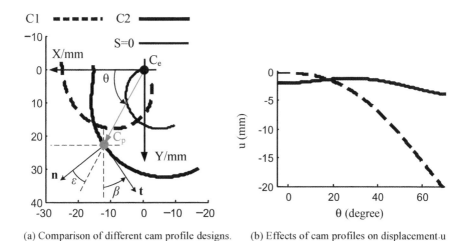

(a) Comparison of different cam profile designs.   (b) Effects of cam profiles on displacement u

Fig. 6.14 Illustrative results of cam profile designs

measurement tolerances has little effects on the calculation of tibia dynamics. As elliptic approximation is employed for the joint geometry, the neglected higher-order terms in the joint dynamics could have contributed to the deviation between experimental and simulated results in Figs. 6.15 and 6.16.

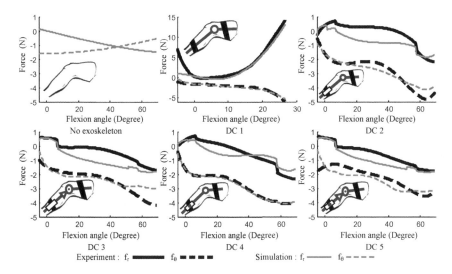

Fig. 6.15 Effects of different design configurations (Table 6.3) on human knee joint internal forces f_r, f_θ

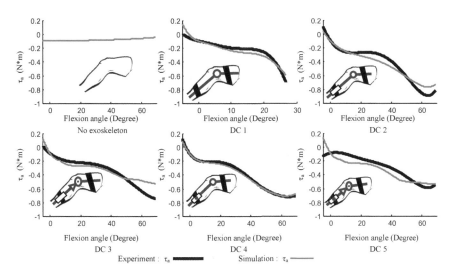

Fig. 6.16 Effects of different design configurations (Table 6.3) on human knee joint internal torque τ_a

Other observations providing insights into the effects of exoskeletons on the internal forces/torque in a knee-joint are summarized as follows:

- The leg without exoskeleton is an open-chain mechanism, and can move freely (with low internal forces and torque experienced in the knee). Due to the

Table 6.5 Comparison of force/torque (mean, RMS, Max Abs values)

	f_r (N)	f_θ (N)	τ_a (N m)
Leg only	(−0.77, 0.96, 1.50)	(−1.23, 1.29, 1.61)	(−0.07, 0.08, 0.09)
DC1 (Exp)	(3.54, 5.10, 14.15)	(−2.10, 2.34, 6.00)	(−0.16, 0.22. 0.70)
(Sim)	(2.11, 3.92, 13.02)	(−2.05, 2.36, 5.29)	(−0.15, 0.24, 0.59)
DC2 (Exp)	(−0.38, 1.03, 2.17)	(−2.82, 3.10, 4.80)	(−0.41, 0.52, 0.89)
(Sim)	(−0.76, 1.04, 1.85)	(−2.80, 2.98, 4.15)	(−0.41, 0.49, 0.77)
DC3 (Exp)	(−0.42, 0.89, 1.71)	(−2.49, 2.70, 4.18)	(−0.34, 0.42, 0.74)
(Sim)	(−0.90, 1.26, 1.85)	(−2.23, 2.36, 3.03)	(−0.30, 0.35, 0.53)
DC4 (Exp)	(−0.63, 1.20, 2.37)	(−2.70, 2.93, 4.10)	(−0.37, 0.46, 0.72)
(Sim)	(−0.63, 0.95, 1.76)	(−−2.75, 2.96, 4.10)	(−0.38, 0.46, 0.71)
DC5 (Exp)	(−0.57, 1.04, 1.77)	(−2.33, 2.45, 3.56)	(−0.30, 0.35, 0.58)
(Sim)	(−0.90, 1.27, 1.85)	(−2.34, 2.50, 3.24)	(−0.30, 0.37, 0.52)

directional components of the lower-leg weight, f_r becomes more negative (tensile) indicating tibia rolls and exerts normal force on femur as the knee flexes while f_θ decreases in magnitude. τ_a decreases to hold the knee in balance because of smaller arm of gravity.

- All five design configurations show that f_θ exhibits an opposite trend from the case with no exoskeleton; this is primarily because the elastic material extends beyond the artificial knee joint, and the exoskeleton exerts its own weight and actuation on the lower leg through the attachment E. In general, simulated (f_θ and τ_a) results agree well with data obtained experimentally. The discrepancies between simulated and experimental f_r suggest that non-linear effects (such as meniscus compliance between femur and tibia) may not be neglected, and that friction in the slider and cam mechanisms is time-varying in the simulation.

- With the zero-DOF *DC1*, the combined leg and exoskeleton forms an over-constrained closed-chain mechanism resulting in a significantly large compressive f_r. Simulation and experiments closely agree except near zero flexion where some discrepancies suggest a violation in the assumption that the attachment at E is linear elastic in simulation. Simulations with nonlinear stiffness k_r and k_θ could offer more realistic f_r and f_θ estimation than with the assumed linear stiffness. In practice, the attachment between the exoskeleton and leg is likely to incorporate some compliance (human skin) that would relax some internal forces but at the expense of uncomfortable slip. Because of the rigid attachment, the elastic material not only extends the artificial knee joint, but also creates the residuary flexion torque τ_e and thus a large tibiofemoral toque τ_a.

- The slider in *DC2*, which offers a translational DOF along the lower link direction, greatly reduces the internal forces and torque in the knee joint, particularly a remarkable decrease in the magnitude of f_r. As observed in the experimental results, because the cam profile was designed to adapt to the changing distance r but not the misalignment θ_E, some compressive f_r can still be observed in certain flexion angles for $DC3$. In addition, the experimental data f_θ in $DC2$ and $DC3$ are somewhat higher than the case without exoskeleton. Some discrepancies observed near final flexion angles are mainly because the nonlinear connection in attachment.

- In $DC4$ and $DC5$, the added pin joint (which sets free the torque θ_E) results in smaller f_r, f_θ and τ_a as compared to $DC2$ and $DC3$.The cam profile used in $DC5$ results in the smallest f_θ and τ_a magnitude among all design configurations. The adaptive design with slider/cam/rotary joint minimizes internal joint forces and torque due to an adaptive human-exoskeleton physical interaction.

- It is worth noting that the artificial model is smaller than and does not have an identical shape as the human knee [1] from which the models were derived for simulating the human-exoskeleton interaction. Theoretically, a cam profile perfectly adaptive to the specific knee motions would be ideal. However, designing such a perfect component could be a difficult task (if not impossible). Some insights into the effect of the cam profile on the internal forces and torque of a knee joint can be gained by comparing the experimental results between the one-DOF ($DC2$, $DC3$) designs and the two-DOF ($DC4$, $DC5$) designs. With a pinned slider that set free the torque angle, the τ_a values in $DC4$ and $DC5$ are 14 and 13% lower than that in $DC2$ and $DC3$ respectively. The addition of a cam mechanism in $DC3$ and $DC5$ results in significantly reducing the forces/torque (f_r, f_θ, τ_a) magnitudes; on an average, (11%, 19%, 23%) and (12%, 17%, 23%) smaller than $DC2$ and $DC4$, respectively. Clearly, $DC5$ offers a smaller (f_θ and τ_a) magnitudes obtained experimentally than those of all other four configurations as compared in Figs. 6.15,6.16 and Table 6.5. The adaptive design with the slider/cam of two-DOF minimizes internal joint forces and torque due to an adaptive human-exoskeleton physical interaction. It is expected that further improvements can be made with some fine-tuning on the design of the cam profile to better match the knee joint. These encouraging experiment results, which capture the geometrical effects on the human-exoskeleton interaction, reasonably confirm that it is feasible to accommodate a limited range of individual size/shape variations (commonly encountered in real human implementation) by sizing the cam and adjusting the mechanical components of the adaptive knee joint exoskeleton.

6.5 Summary

In this chapter, a general method for mathematical modeling a biological joint has been introduced, which provides a better understanding on the interaction between natural joints and artificial mechanisms for design and control of bio-inspired exoskeletons.

With the aid of published MRI data, the ellipsoid-based bio-joint model has been shown to offer a physically more accurate account of both rolling and sliding motions within a biological joint than a geometrically simple pin-joint approximation or methods based on multiple circles and lines. The bio-joint model shows that the sliding–rolling displacement ratio is not a constant but has an average value consistent with the published measurements and its mathematically differentiable property facilitates the analysis of rolling/sliding velocity.

Five knee exoskeletons are designed with combinations of adaptive kinematic components, such as a pin, slider and cam. Dynamic analysis is performed to investigate the effects of different design configurations on the joint internal forces and torque. Experimental findings suggest that incorporating a pin slider/cam can effectively minimize internal joint forces and torque from the human-exoskeleton interaction.

References

1. H. Iwaki, V. Pinskerova, M.A.R. Freeman, Tibiofemoral movement 1: the shapes and relative movements of the femur and tibia in the unloaded cadaver knee. J. Bone Joint Surg. **82B**(8), 1189–1195 (2000)
2. T. Nomiyama, A. Lawi, T. Katsuhara, S. Hirokawa, Model analysis of lower limb at deep knee flexion, in *Proceedings of the International Conference on Electrical Engineering and Informatics*, Institut Teknologi Bandung, Indonesia, 2007
3. K.-M. Lee, J. Guo, Kinematic and dynamic analysis of an anatomically based knee joint. J. Biomech. **43**(7), 1231–1236 (2010)
4. J.-F. Zhang, Y.-M. Dong, C.-J. Yang, Y. Geng, Y. Chen, Y. Yang, 5-link model based gait trajectory adaption control strategies of the gait rehabilitation exoskeleton for post-stroke patients. Mechatronics **20**(3), 368–376 (2010)
5. M. Damavandi, N. Farahpour, P. Allard, Determination of body segment masses and centers of mass using a force plate method in individuals of different morphology. Med. Eng. Phys. **31**(9), 1187–1194 (2009)
6. Z.-K. Ling, H.-Q. Guo, S. Boersma, Analytical study on the kinematic and dynamic behaviors of a knee joint. Med. Eng. Phys. **19**(1), 29–36 (1997)

Chapter 7
Musculoskeletal Modeling

Employing the flexible elements and bio-joint constraints in Chap. 3, this chapter models a poultry musculo-skeleton and investigates the carcass musculoskeletal deformations under wing manipulations to facilitate the deboning of chicken breast meat. A framework of a musculoskeletal model is provided with a compliant beam model for bones and a constitutive model for tendon/ligaments. Numerical verification is presented for the compliant beam model. The soft-tissue model is validated by experiments and values of its coefficients are determined. This musculoskeletal model is employed to investigate the bio-structural deformations, and the analysis will contribute to the wing manipulator design and related controller implementation.

7.1 Musculoskeletal System

A chicken skeleton is illustrated in Fig. 7.1, where of particular interest here is the complicated tripod-like structure formed by the three bones (coracoid, clavicle and scapula) and two joints; namely, the joint between the coracoid and keel bone, and the shoulder joint. Because of the joint flexibility, wing manipulation could result in a significant shoulder displacement which would affect the initial cut position and the final yield of meat. The effect of bio-joint constraint on the shoulder position is investigated by comparing against a typical ball joint-socket approximation. In this study, the following assumptions are made:

(A1) The carcass is properly loaded on the cone such that the symmetric plane of the carcass coincides with that of the cone, and the rib cage does not rotate on the cone. In this way, the rib cage and keel bone are assumed to be rigid with respect to the cone.

© Huazhong University of Science and Technology Press, Wuhan and Springer
Nature Singapore Pte Ltd. 2019
J. Guo and K.-M Lee, *Flexonics for Manufacturing and Robotics*, Research on
Intelligent Manufacturing, https://doi.org/10.1007/978-981-13-2667-7_7

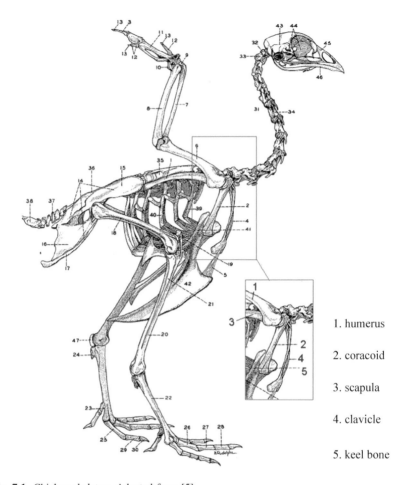

1. humerus

2. coracoid

3. scapula

4. clavicle

5. keel bone

Fig. 7.1 Chicken skeleton. Adapted from [5]

(A2) The coracoid-keel and shoulder joints can be characterized as contacts
between two ellipsoids, thus can be modeled as bio-joint constraints
(Sect. 3.4) on the flexible clavicle. The clavicle material property is isotropic and linear elastically.

(A3) All the ligaments/tendons within a bird carcass are of the same material so
that their deformation behavior can be described by one general characteristic relation [1]. The soft tissue material is anisotropic and incompressible; this assumption is based on the knowledge of the high percentage
of water content within the soft tissue and its longitudinal fiber bundle
structure.

7.1.1 Coordinates

To describe the pulling δ and twisting θ motions of the humerus, the kinematics is defined in Fig. 7.2. The reference coordinate system O is set on the keel bone where the prong plugs in. The X and Z axes (of frame O) are on the symmetric plane of the carcass; the Z axis points upwards while the X axis is the direction that the cone moves toward. The frames, O_c and O_s, are the local coordinate systems at the coracoid-keel and the shoulder joints, respectively. The Z_c axis is the longitudinal axis of the coracoid; X_c is the normal to the plane defined by the two intersecting axes of the coracoids. As shown in Fig. 7.2, O_cO_s is in the direction of the Z_c axis, and defines the length of the coracoid. The frames $O_sX_sY_sZ_s$ and OXYZ are parallel and related only with a transitional transformation. The local coordinate manipulating frame O_m is attached at the other end of the humerus with its z_m-axis pointing along the humerus longitudinal axis. In Fig. 7.2, the attachment points of the ligaments on the coracoid and scapula are denoted as A, B and C, respectively; and the lengths and directions are characterized by the vectors $\mathbf{L_A}$, $\mathbf{L_B}$ and $\mathbf{L_C}$ in the reference frame OXYZ.

Since the bases of the clavicle is attached to the shoulders, which displace and rotate with the coracoid-keel joint and are subjected to the tendon forces, results of the bio-joint constraint serves as boundary conditions for the flexible clavicle (modeled with the compliant beam model) in analyzing the deformations of the tripod-like structure to predict shoulder displacement under wing manipulation.

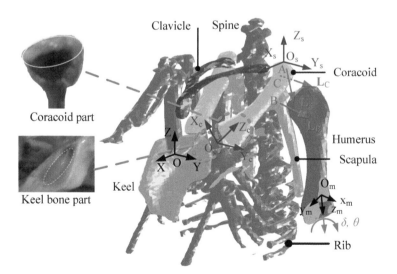

(A. Coracohumeral, B. Scapulohumeral, C. Interfibrous ligaments)

Fig. 7.2 Ligament-skeletal structure of a chicken carcass

7.1.2 Bio-joint Constraint

In the bio-joint model, O_c is defined as the geometric center of the ellipse that models the portion of the coracoid as shown in Fig. 7.2. The coordinate transformation from O to O_c involves two rotations (θ_y followed by θ_x about Y and X_c, respectively) and a translation (O to O_s), and it is given by

$$\mathbf{x}_{O_c} = [\mathbf{R}]\mathbf{x}_O + \mathbf{p}_{co} \qquad (7.1)$$

where $\mathbf{R}$ is a rotational matrix, $\mathbf{p}_{co}$ is the displacement vector from O_c to O.

Figure 7.2 shows the ellipses approximating the contact parts within the coracoid-keel joint. Dimensions of the joints and bones are listed in Table 7.1. The effect of the coracoid-keel joint rotation (characterized by the rotational variables θ_x and θ_y) is illustrated numerically on the position changes of the tripod-like structure. The simulations are based on typical dimensions experimentally measured from commercial broilers (meat chickens). As shown in Figs. 7.3 and 7.4, the contact pair making up the shoulder joint can be modeled as a combination of an ellipsoid and an elliptical cylinder. Principal axis lengths of the 3D ellipsoid are given in Table 7.1 for the simulation.

When tensioning the ligaments and tendon for the first cut in deboning the chicken breast meat, the humerus is pulled downward the tripod-like structure deforms as a result of the joint rotations (θ_x and θ_y), where the nominal dimensions are given in Table 7.1. To offer an intuitive insight to the effect of $\Delta\theta_x$ and $\Delta\theta_y$ (deviations from the nominal values) on the prediction of shoulder positions (with respect to the reference coordinate system O), Figs. 7.3 and 7.4 compare the results calculated with the bio-joint model and the ball joint approximation, where the following percentage error is employed to quantify the difference,

$$\%Error = 100\% \times (\Delta d_e / \Delta d_{bio})$$

Table 7.1 Dimensions of coracoid-keel joint and bones

Coracoid-keel joint (mm)		Shoulder joint (mm)	
Coracoid	9.2, 3.1, 2.3	Coracoid	2.6, 6.6, ∞
Keel	10.2, 4.1, 1.9	Humerus	9.3, 7.0, 5.6
Bone	Length (mm)	Position	Value
Coracoid	38.3	O_c (mm)[a]	(-15.0, -10, 20.4)
Humerus	80.7	θ_x	$\pi/12$
Scapula	75.0	θ_y	$\pi/4$
Sliding velocity between the two parts in bio-joint = 1 mm/s			

[a]O_c's coordinates are presented in the world frame O

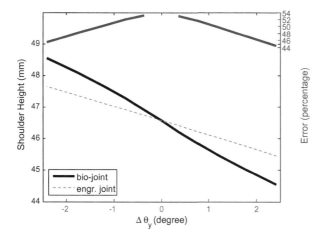

Fig. 7.3 Change of shoulder height due to $\Delta\theta_y$

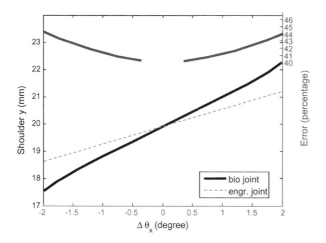

Fig. 7.4 Change of shoulder position due to $\Delta\theta_x$

where Δd_{bio} is the deviation from the nominal position as predicted by the bio-joint model; and Δd_e is the difference between the results predicted by the two models. In Figs. 7.3 and 7.4, the percentage errors near the nominal position ($\Delta\theta_x = \Delta\theta_y = 0$) are not calculated to avoid division by zero.

Some observations can be made from Figs. 7.3 and 7.4:

(1) In Fig. 7.3, the error decreases as the rotation angle becomes larger. This is because of the error definition and the nonlinear effect of the bio-joint model; in other words, Δd_{bio} increases at a faster rate than Δd_e.

(2) In general, the shoulder deforms nonlinearly from its nominal position even in a small angle rotation.

(3) The shoulder joint is possible to attain limited translational motion of the humerus relative to the fixed carcass (in addition to the three rotational DOFs) due to the deformability of the connective tissues. The ball joint approximation, which assumes a fixed center at O_c, does not account the transitional motion as can be visualized in Case 2(b) in Fig. 3.17. Hence, the ball-socket approximation predicts a linear relation in small angle rotation about the nominal position. The significantly large Δd_e error (over 40%) implies that the ball joint approximation is inadequate to characterize the coracoid-keel joint and its associated musculoskeletal kinematics. The bio-joint model with two 3D ellipsoids provides a means to account for the transitional motion of O_c within the joint clearance.

7.1.3   Clavicle Model

Section 7.1.2 provides the relationship between the coracoid rotation ($\Delta\theta_x$, $\Delta\theta_y$) and the shoulder displacement. This in turn provides a means to relate the rotational matrix $\mathbf{R}$ to the absolute position $\mathbf{x}_0$ of the shoulder (where the clavicle is attached). Hence, the boundary conditions for (3.1) are given by

$$s = 0 \quad R_{11} = 1, R_{12} = 0, R_{13} = 0, \varphi = 0, x_1 = x_1^{(0)}, x_2 = x_2^{(0)}, x_3 = x_3^{(0)}$$
$$s = 1 \quad F_1, F_2, F_3, M_1, M_2, M_3$$

Because of the V-shape geometry of the clavicle, Fig. 7.5a shows one half of the clavicle which is separated by the symmetric plane S (OXZ in Fig. 7.2). Then the clavicle bone is modeled as a cantilever beam mounted at point O_c (with axis X_c pointing along the bone axis and Z_c being the same as Z). The clavicle is subjected to force F_c and moment M_c from the shoulder as well as the distributed force from the breast meat. In Fig. 7.5a, two meat elements along the fiber direction are presented on both sides of the clavicle. As the end of the clavicle is pulled/twisted by F_c and M_c, one element is in tension f_{mt} while the other is in compression f_{mc}, resulting in an effective distributed force $q_c (= f' + f'')$ along the bone, where $f' \approx \varphi_m f_{mt}$ and $f'' \approx \varphi_m f_{mc}$. The angle φ_m is defined as the slope angle change per fiber length, which is very small for a smooth breast meat surface.

Certain assumptions are made in the following formulation:

(A4) The bone material is assumed to be isotropic and linear elastic, because of its small dimension and limited deflection during the wing manipulations.

(A5) The bone deformations in the X_c and Z_c directions are negligible compared to the deflection in the Y_c direction, because the bone is relatively rigid along the longitudinal axis and the clavicle tip (point O_c) can only move in the symmetric plane S to adapt to possible vertical deflections due to the shoulder deformations.

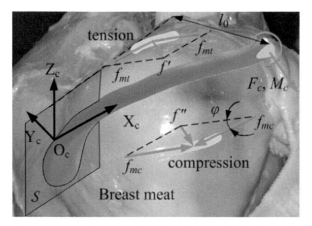

(a) Local coordinate and loadings for one half of clavicle.

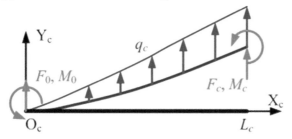

(b) Compliant beam formulation.

Fig. 7.5 Clavicle deformation

(A6) The outer surface of breast meat is stress free initially, and deforms under wing manipulations like an elastic foundation of linear springs. Specifically, the distributed force is proportional to the deformation displacement. The value of φ_m is assumed to be 0.005 in radians.

Figure 7.5b shows the free body diagram of the clavicle, where the initial length is L_c. For simplicity, the subscript "c" in the coordinates X_c and Y_c is dropped, and the governing equation of the compliant beam model is given by

$$EI y'' = -M_0 + F_0 x + \int_0^x (x - \xi) q_c d\xi \tag{7.2a}$$

where the double primes refer to the second derivative with respect to x, the force F_0 and moment M_0 at $x = 0$ can be obtained at equilibrium:

$$F_0 = -\int_0^{L_c} q_c d\xi - F_c$$

$$M_0 = -\int_0^{L_c} \xi q_c d\xi - F_c L_c - M_c$$

Then (7.2a) is rewritten as

$$EIy'' = \int_{L_c}^{x} (x - \xi)q_c d\xi + F_c(L_c - x) + M_c \qquad (7.2b)$$

and the third and fourth order derivatives are obtained as

$$EIy''' = \int_{L_c}^{x} q_c d\xi - F_c \qquad (7.2c)$$

$$EIy'''' = q_c \qquad (7.2d)$$

If denoting $\mathbf{Y} = [y \, y' \, y'' \, y''']^{\mathrm{T}}$, the above equations can be combined into a compact form

$$\mathbf{Y}' = \mathbf{F} \qquad (7.3)$$

with $\mathbf{F} = \begin{bmatrix} \mathbf{0} & \mathbf{I}_{3\times3} \\ q_c/EI & \mathbf{0}^T \end{bmatrix}$

The boundary conditions are determined from the cantilever constraint and soft tissue loads:

$$y(0) = 0, \ y'(0) = 0 \qquad (7.4a, b)$$

$$EIy''(L_c) = M_c, \ EIy'''(L_c) = -F_c \qquad (7.4c, d)$$

This boundary value problem (BVP) can be readily solved by the shooting method.

Closed form solution

The boundary value problem is first recast into an IVP with initial conditions given in (7.4a,b) and (7.4e,f):

$$EIy''(0) = \int_0^{L_c} \xi q_c d\xi + F_c L_c + M_c \qquad (7.4e)$$

$$EIy'''(0) = -\int_0^{L_c} q_c d\xi - F_c \qquad (7.4f)$$

Based on the assumption (A6) of an elastic foundation, the functional form of q_c is taken as

$$q_c = k_m y \qquad (7.5)$$

where k_m is an effective elastic constant. Substituting (7.5) into (7.2d), the general solution for $EIy'''' = k_m y$ is

$$y = A_1 e^{\lambda x} + A_2 e^{-\lambda x} + A_3 \cos \lambda x + A_4 \sin \lambda x \qquad (7.6)$$

where $\lambda = (k_m/EI)^{1/4}$ and A_i's (i = 1, 2, 3 and 4) are coefficients to be determined by the initial conditions at $x = 0$. By substituting (7.5) and (7.6) into (7.4a,b,e,f), four algebraic equations of $\mathbf{A} = [A_1 \, A_2 \, A_3 \, A_4]^T$ can be obtained and written in a matrix form

$$\mathbf{M}_A \mathbf{A} = \mathbf{b}_A \qquad (7.7)$$

where $\mathbf{b}_A$ and $\mathbf{M}_A$ are given as

$$\mathbf{b}_A = [0 \quad 0 \quad -F_c \quad F_c L_c + M_c]^T$$

$$\mathbf{M}_A = \begin{bmatrix} 1 & 1 & 1 & 0 \\ \lambda & -\lambda & 0 & \lambda \\ EI\lambda^3 & -EI\lambda^3 & 0 & -EI\lambda^3 \\ EI\lambda^2 & EI\lambda^2 & -EI\lambda^2 & 0 \end{bmatrix} + k_m \begin{bmatrix} \mathbf{0}^T \\ \mathbf{0}^T \\ \boldsymbol{\alpha}^T \\ \boldsymbol{\beta}^T \end{bmatrix}$$

with

$$\boldsymbol{\alpha} = \frac{1}{\lambda} \left[-1 + e^{\lambda L_c} \quad 1 - e^{-\lambda L_c} \quad \sin \lambda L_c \quad 1 - \cos \lambda L_c \right]^T$$

$$\boldsymbol{\beta} = \frac{1}{\lambda^2} \begin{bmatrix} 1 + e^{\lambda L_c}(-1 + \lambda L_c) \\ 1 - e^{-\lambda L_c}(1 + \lambda L_c) \\ -1 + \cos \lambda L_c + \lambda L_c \sin \lambda L_c \\ -\lambda L_c \cos \lambda L_c + \sin \lambda L_c \end{bmatrix}$$

Then the closed form solution can be obtained by solving A_i's from (7.7) and substituting them into (7.6). On the other hand, if the functional form of q_c is taken as (7.5′),

$$q_c = k_m x \qquad (7.5')$$

The closed form solution is given as follows:

$$y = -\frac{k_m}{120EI}x^5 + \frac{k_mL_c^2 + 2F_c}{12EI}x^3 + \frac{3M_c + 3f_cL_c - k_mL_c^3}{6EI}x^2 \qquad (7.6')$$

It will be shown that as the loadings increase, the solution (7.6) can be approximated by (7.6′) which is much easier for further investigation of dimension effects.

The elastic foundation assumption for modeling the breast meat is employed as a lumped parameter approach. But the numerical value of k_m can be estimated based on theoretical derivation and experiment data. This starts with the stress-strain relation of meat:

$$\sigma_m = E_m\varepsilon_m \qquad (7.8)$$

where E_m is the elastic modulus of meat, σ_m and ε_m are longitudinal stress and strain along the fiber direction. Denoting the minor axis length of the clavicle cross section as $2b$, one half of the shoulder width as l_0, and the Poisson ratio as $\upsilon = 0.5$, the distributed load on the clavicle q_c and strain in the lateral direction ε'_m can be expressed as

$$q_c = \varphi_m\sigma_m \cdot 2b \qquad (7.9)$$

$$\varepsilon'_m = \frac{y}{l_0} = \upsilon\varepsilon_m \qquad (7.10)$$

Based on (7.5), (7.7)–(7.9), the equivalent elastic constant can be estimated as

$$k_m = \frac{2\varphi_m bE_m}{\upsilon l_0} \qquad (7.11)$$

7.1.4   Soft Tissue Mechanics

Figure 7.6 shows the schematic structure of ligaments or tendons, where the soft tissue is divided into fiber bundles on hierarchy levels [2]. Since the concepts of stress and strain are based on local deformations, the force-extension relations of ligaments and tendons with various sizes are readily obtained through integration if the characteristic relation of each collagen is available. This general characteristic relation is very helpful in modeling different ligaments/tendons within one bird as well as in a large sample of birds by accounting for the variable size.

Based on the assumption (A3), the characteristic relation is given by

$$\sigma = k_2e^{k_1\varepsilon} \qquad (7.12)$$

where σ is the stress; ε is the longitudinal strain of the ligament under uni-axial extension; and k_1 and k_2 are constants to be determined experimentally.

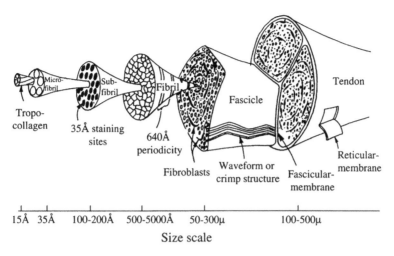

Fig. 7.6 Structural hierarchy of ligament or tendon [2]

Equation (7.12) can be transformed into the following linear logarithmic form for determining k_1 and k_2 using the linear regression method:

$$\log \sigma = k_1 \varepsilon + \log k_2 \tag{7.13}$$

Due to the assumption of incompressible tissues, the volume will not change before and after deformations. Denoting the initial cross section area as A_0, the current cross section area can be obtained by

$$A = A_0/(1+\varepsilon) \tag{7.14}$$

Since $\sigma = f/A$, $\varepsilon = \Delta/L_0$, where Δ is the stretch and L_0 is the initial length, the relation between the stretch Δ and the tensile force f acting on the ligament is given by

$$f = \frac{A_0}{1+\Delta/L_0} k_1 e^{k_2 \Delta/L_0} \tag{7.15}$$

It is noted that the elastic modulus E of the clavicle and the two parameters, k_1 and k_2, for soft tissues in (7.6) and (7.15) are to be determined in experiment.

7.2 Experimental Investigation

Since the material properties of the clavicle bone and the ligament are not available, the clavicle elastic modulus in (7.6) and the ligament parameters in Eq. (7.15) were determined from two sets of experiments. Although the parameters are determined by the simple pulling tests, the resulting models are valid for nonlinear analysis of the musculoskeletal structure. Specifically, the clavicle deformations are mainly affected by the nonlinear curved-bone geometry even though the linear elastic property is assumed where only the elastic modulus E is measured. On the other hand, the ligament deformations are governed by the nonlinear material property, where two parameters k_1 and k_2 are to be determined.

7.2.1   Elastic Modulus of Clavicle

This section determines the elastic modulus of clavicles in experiment. Figure 7.7 shows an experimental setup based on a commercial linear motor driven stage, where a clavicle bone was mounted on the linear slider while its tip was rigidly tied to a fixed screw by a metal string. The screw height was adjusted for different specimens to maintain a horizontal pulling force through the string. As the linear slider pulled in the right direction, the clavicle deflected as a cantilever beam. Since the metal string is much stiffer than the flexible clavicles, the string elongation is negligible compared to the bone deflections. So the measured slider displacementcan be regarded as the clavicle tip deflection. Based on the previous analysis, the vertical displacement of the clavicle is less than 7.9 mm, and the metal string length is 60 mm, so the rotation of the string is within 7.5°, leading to the assumption that the applied force on the clavicle tip is horizontal. At equilibrium, the pulling force can be interpreted from the input voltage to the linear motor.

The pulling force from the linear motor was calibrated by a spring with one end fixed and the other end mounted on the slider as shown in Fig. 7.8. The calibration curve of the electric spring is given by (7.16):

$$F = \begin{cases} 1.82V^2 - 0.27V + 0.09 & \text{if } V \leq 1 \\ 3.37V - 1.73 & \text{if } V > 1 \end{cases} \tag{7.16}$$

The curve exhibits a linear force-voltage relationship when V is larger than 1 V. Because the static friction is estimated as 1.73 N, the nonlinear relation noticeably

Fig. 7.7 Experimental setup with a calibrated linear motor

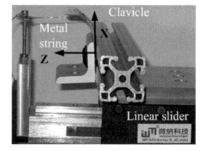

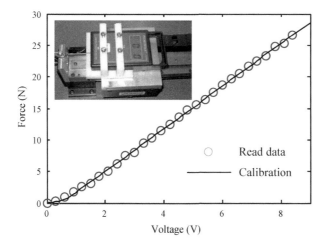

Fig. 7.8 Calibration of the linear motor for the force-voltage relation

dominates for the voltage less than 1 V. In the experiment, the linear motor pulled the clavicle with a ramped current input. The force can be calculated from the input voltage using (7.16) and the clavicle-tip deflection was measured by the encoder on the linear stage.

Figure 7.9 shows the bone-deflection displacement and input force profiles for two groups, samples 1–4 of intact clavicles and samples 5–8 of half clavicles. As shown in Fig. 7.9a, all samples (1–4) deformed within the ultimate strength, while the horizontal parts in Fig. 7.9b indicate the clavicles were broken and the breaking strength is estimated as about 6 N.

Figures 7.10 and 7.11 compare relations between the pulling force and the tip deflection from simulation and experiment. The elastic modulus for all eight samples can be obtained with an average value of 2.7816 ± 1.1803 GPa. Errors can be introduced by defects occur in the sample preparation. Figure 7.11 also shows that the clavicles broke progressively so that the elastic modulus changed nonlinearly with the increasing pulling force.

7.2.2 Ligament Mechanics

To determine the appropriate trajectory and forces of wing manipulations for presenting the ligaments to the cutter, the ligaments are modeled as a non-linear spring in the form suggested by (7.15) which is validated against the experimental data [3]. As shown in Fig. 7.13a, the coracohumeralis ligament was chosen as the test sample considering its size, location, and ease of singulation. The other major ligaments are difficult to remove without damages. In an effort not to alter the

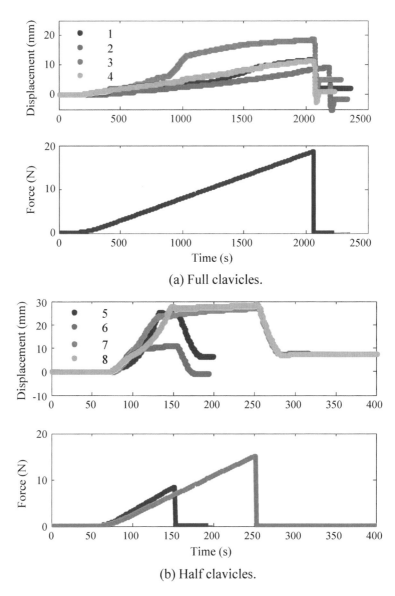

(a) Full clavicles.

(b) Half clavicles.

Fig. 7.9 Relation between pulling force and deflection on clavicles

ligament characteristics, the ligament was not separated from either the humerus or the coracoid. By retaining the bone connection on both ends of the ligament, it is convenient to apply a tension on the sample without complicated clamping devices. Experimental data were obtained from uniaxial extension at a constant pulling velocity of 0.5 mm/s on eight samples [3]: the cross section area was regarded as an ellipse and the dimensions (listed in Table 7.2) were measured by a caliper; the

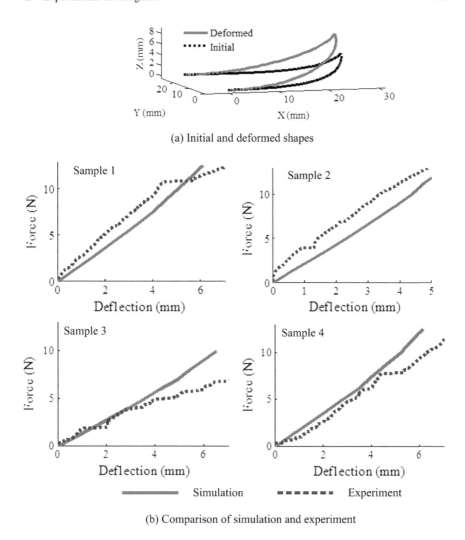

(a) Initial and deformed shapes

(b) Comparison of simulation and experiment

Fig. 7.10   Tests on samples of full clavicles

ABB robot pulled the humerus at a very low constant speed of 0.5 mm/s, so the tested sample can be regarded in a quasi-static state; the stretch was obtained from the product of the pulling speed and the time, and the applying tensile force was measured by the force sensor. Figure 7.13a shows the experiment results of the stretch and tensile force. Since the data of Sample A do not fall in the 95% confidence interval, this data is rejected and the average values together with ±95% variation are calculated based on the other seven samples. It is clear that data from biological objects have a very large variation (up to 50%) and the calculated results based on the seven samples are

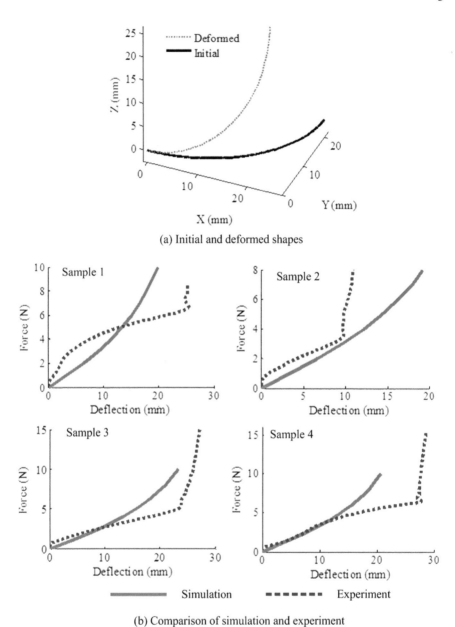

(a) Initial and deformed shapes

(b) Comparison of simulation and experiment

Fig. 7.11 Tests on samples of half clavicles

Table 7.2 Force sensor and sample dimensions

ATI Mini 40—US-5-10			
Maximum (N, N m)	$F_{x,y} = 22.24$	$F_z = 44.48$	$T_{x,y,z} = 112.98$
Resolution (N, N m)	$F_{x,y} = 0.0014$	$F_z = 0.0028$	$T_{x,y,z} = 0.0035$
Sample[a]	A	B	C	D
A_0 (mm^2)	73.22	83.99	60.30	80.49
L_0 (mm)	20.60	22.06	18.69	21.59
Sample[a]	E	F	G	H
A_0 (mm^2)	104.5	73.80	81.02	70.15
L_0 (mm)	24.60	20.70	21.67	20.16

[a]Average $A_0 = 69.04$ mm^2, $L_0 = 20$ mm

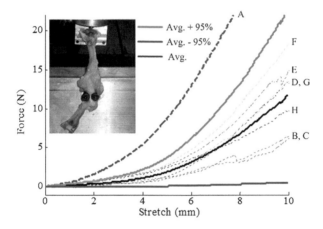

Fig. 7.12 Uniaxial extension of ligaments [3]

$$k_1 = 9.9246 \pm 1.9776, \quad k_2 = 0.0027 \pm 0.0019$$

Figure 7.13a compares the force and stretch relations obtained from experiment and the proposed model (7.15) with nominal values $k_1 = 9.4377$ and $k_2 = 0.0025$. Given the large variations in Table 7.2 and Fig. 7.12 among samples, the proposed ligament model agrees well with experimental data over a relatively large range of strain (about 0.5). The outlier of the first sample could be due to some unknown causes in the original data as indicated in Fig. 7.12. One explanation would be that the bird was injured on the shoulder and the ligament become stiffer; similar things could have happened to samples E and F. Deviations in the sample B and C are due

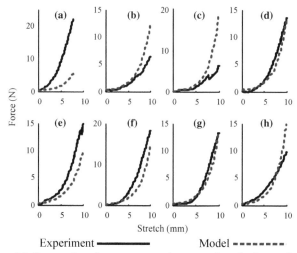

(a) Comparison between experiment and analysis results.

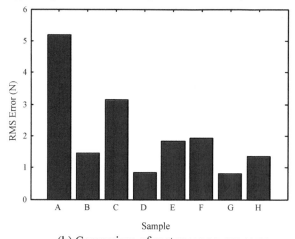

(b) Comparison of root mean square error.

Fig. 7.13 Ligament/tendon characteristic relation

to the local damages of the fiber bundles during the extension. It is valuable to point out that models formulated with scalable variables, such as length or cross section area, can be accurately developed for a specific natural product by relating these scalable variables to its overall size or weight proportionally. Figure 7.13b compares the root mean square error in the applying force, with average value for the Sample B–H being about 1.6 N.

7.3 Illustrative Application to Wing Manipulation

The illustrative example is motivated from poultry industry, where boneless breast meat is removed from chicken carcasses for subsequent meat processing [4]. The job requires pulling and then twisting a wing to sever the ligaments/tendons for deboning the meat typically at a rate of 1 bird/second. This repetitive job is a potential cause of cumulative trauma disorder, and thus a candidate for automation. A critical part of this process is the need to manipulate both wings to tension the ligaments and tendon before severing them as illustrated in Fig. 7.14, which leads the following questions to be answered: (1) where are the ligaments and tendon located? (2) How much force and torque are required to manipulate the wings? (3) In what directions should the force and torque be applied? Most of the early research effort focused on developing a method (based primarily on vision sensing feedback) to position the cutting blade for the initial insertion. A good understanding of the important factors (such as the structural compliance due to joint clearance and connecting soft tissues) contributing to the whole carcass deformation is essential to the precision deboning. In this book, a musculoskeletal structure of a chicken shoulder is modeled as a multi-body compliant mechanism with bio-joints to predict the locations of ligaments/tendon and required manipulating forces under large deformation of a carcass. This mechanism differs from others in the sense that rigid bodies (bones) and compliant links (tiny bones/soft tissues) are not connected in series but in a 3D topology. The deformation of this compliant bio-structure, together with non-uniform joint constraints, will be analyzed using the model for multi-body compliant mechanisms.

Figure 7.14a illustrates the bio-structure consisting of the shoulder bones and three ligaments (indicated as A, B, C in Fig. 7.2) connecting the humerus to the three shoulder bones; coracoid, clavicle and scapula. The shoulder joint has three rotational DOFs and due to the deformability of the connective tissues; it is possible to attain limited translational motion of the humerus relative to the fixed carcass. The breast-meat removal operation consists of two major cuts as illustrated in Fig. 7.14b. The first cut, notably the most difficult to automate, is a cut through the shoulder joint severing the two main ligaments (A and C). Once the two ligaments have been cut, the second cut continues the incision from the back of the shoulder down through the third ligament B, and along the scapula bone. After the knife exits at the base of the scapula the breast-meat can be removed. This is accomplished by a robot which pulls and twists on both wings before removing the wings and breast meat from the carcass. Figure 7.14c, d show the osculating parts of the coracoid and humerus in the shoulder joint.

Figure 7.15 shows the automated wing manipulation (AWM) system developed at Georgia Tech [3] for tensioning the ligaments/tendon of a chicken front-half for subsequent cutting and harvesting the chicken breast meat, where the AWM with a 6 DOF force/torque sensor is mounted on an ABB robot arm. As the AWM system pulls or twists the chicken wing, significant deformations on the shoulder were observed. This gives rise to significant errors in locating the shoulder joint (and thus the blade insertion location) which further deteriorate the yield/quality of deboned

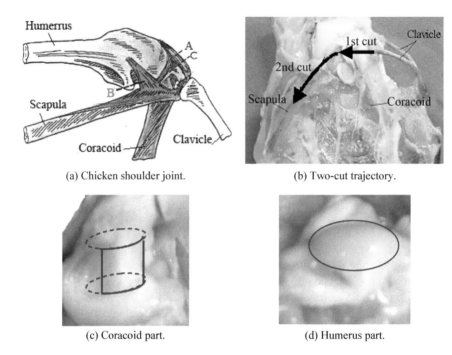

(a) Chicken shoulder joint.   (b) Two-cut trajectory.

(c) Coracoid part.   (d) Humerus part.

Fig. 7.14 Ligament-skeletal structure of a chicken-shoulder joint

breast meat in precision cutting. In order to predict the chicken carcass deformations under wing manipulation, a musculoskeletal model is needed to be implemented on the mechanical meat harvester to guide the cutting blade.

Applications of the presented musculoskeletal model are illustrated using two wing manipulation examples:

Pulling $\delta = 10$ mm along the direction of 0.5Y-0.866Z defined in the reference frame OXYZ as shown in Fig. 7.2.

Twisting $\theta = 90°$ around the humerus longitudinal axis z_m.

Table 7.3 lists the positions of all three ligaments and tendon, which are measured from a scanned geometry of a real chicken front-half. Since the ligaments/ tendon are along different directions, the manipulator displacement is projected along L_i (i = A, B and C) for estimating their individual elongations. The ligament forces f_i can then be calculated from (7.15); and their resulting force F_c and moment M_c can be applied to (7.6) to determine the shoulder displacements in the reference frame. As indicated from the simulation results, the pulling manipulation significantly tensions the ligaments A and C affecting the shoulder position in all directions, while the twisting motion mainly tensions ligament B and displaces the shoulder on the XY plane.

The wing manipulation tensions the ligaments and tendon to facilitate the cutting process. Once the stress within the soft tissues reaches a critical value, it is

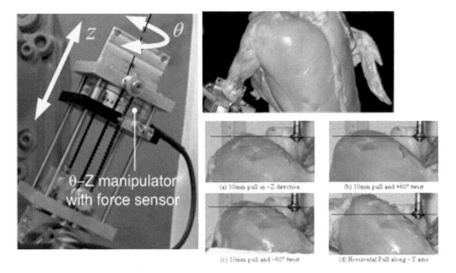

Fig. 7.15 Observations of wing manipulation on shoulder location

Table 7.3 Measured data and simulation results

Ligaments	Attachment point	Vector L_i (mm)	Cross-section area A (mm^2)	
A	−58.85, 19.72, 31.03	−7.23, 12.46, −19.02	69.04	
B	−58.36, 14.81, 22.97	−7.8, 18.09, −5.46	50.68	
C	−60.56, 16.14, −0.42	−3.59, 13.05, −0.77	22.29	
Pulling δ =10 mm	Ligament forces (N)	$f_A = 5.3$	$f_B = 2.1$	$f_C = 1.6$
	Loadings on shoulder	$F_c = 6.2$ N	$M_c = -0.011$ N mm	
	Shoulder disp. (mm)	$u_X = 0.9$	$u_Y = 2.6$	$u_Z = 8.7$
Twisting $\theta = 90°$	Ligament force (N)	$f_A = 0$	$f_B = 3.44$	$f_C = 0$
	Loadings on shoulder	$F_c = 1.2$ N	$M_c = -0.017$ N mm	
	Shoulder disp. (mm)	$u_X = 0.5$	$u_Y = 1.4$	$u_Z = 0$

anticipated to be easily severed. Correspondingly there exists a critical strain from (7.12). Under assumption (A3) in Sect. 7.1, this critical stress or strain would be the same for different birds because it is the mechanical property of soft tissues. However, (7.15) indicates that the applying force would be dependent on the cross-section area of soft tissues, A_0, which is assumed to be proportional to the square of the overall bird feature dimension, such as the half shoulder width l_0. As a result, if a bird size is 10% larger than the reference model size, the required force will become 21% larger.

On the other hand, the shoulder will displace and imprecise cut will occur due to error of blade insertion location as the wing is manipulated. Given the desired manipulating force, (7.6) can be used to predict the shoulder displacement. It is noted that x is proportional to l_0, area moment of inertia I is on the order of l_0^4, By analyzing each of the coefficients of F_c, M_c and k_m, it is found that they are proportional to $1/l_0$, $1/l_0^2$ and $1(l_0)$, respectively, indicating that: effects of the meat deformation is independent on the bird dimension. However, the effects of the external loadings are dependent on the dimension variation: if the bird is 10% larger than the reference model size, the same pulling force will give rise to 11% reduction in shoulder displacement, while the same twisting moment will cause 23% reduction in displacement.

7.4 Summary

This chapter has discussed a dimension-based method to characterize bone and soft tissue deformation by accounting for the large size variation of natural products. A compliant beam model is employed for the clavicle bone deformation and a closed-form solution is obtained by assuming elastic foundation of breast meat. The solution is verified by the numerical multiple shooting method and an approximated polynomial solution is adopted for estimation of size variation effects on bone deformation. Analysis justifies this approach by showing that the approximation error vanishes as the external loadings increase. An exponential characteristic relation is used to capture highly nonlinear elastic property of soft tissues. Given the large variation of force profiles among specimens, the proposed model agrees well with experiment results. Finally, the musculoskeletal model is applied in wing manipulation to analyze the effects of size variation on the required manipulating force and shoulder deformations. This musculoskeletal model can be potentially used to develop design criteria to automate the process of de-boning chicken breast-meat. While this chapter is written in the context of poultry meat de-boning, the method can be used for other bio-tissues, joints, and systems.

References

1. Y.C.B. Fung, Elasticity of soft tissues in simple elongation. Am. J. Physiol. **213**(6), 1532–1544 (1967)
2. J. Kastelic, I. Palley, E. Baer, The multicomposite ultrastructure of tendon. Conn. Tiss. Res. **6**, 11–23 (1978)
3. M.R. Claffee, *The Effects of Wing Manipulation on Automated Cutting of Biological Materials.* Master, Mechanical Engineering, Georgia Institute of Technology, Atlanta, (2006)
4. W. Daley, T. He, K.-M. Lee, M. Sandlin, Modeling of the natural product deboning process using biological, in *Proceedings of IEEE/ASME International Conference on Advanced Intelligent Mechatronics (AIM)*, (1999), pp. 49–54
5. H.E. Evans, *Guide to the Study and Dissection of the Chicken* (New York State Veterinary College, Cornell University, Ithaca, New York, USA, 1961)

Printed by Printforce, the Netherlands